VISION TOMORROW

In this his first novel, Edmund Harold takes us on a journey through time, which leaves a chill within the self, as it illustrates one man's involvement in prophecy and mystical communication. The journey is commenced in the dim mists of time upon the sunken continent of Atlantis, finding its sequel in the twenty-third century.

As it unfolds, the tale graphically illustrates the earthquakes, tidal waves, and global tumult, which are said to lie ahead of man before the closing of the twentieth century.

GW00675464

By the same author:
Master Your Vibration

VISION TOMORROW

Edmund Harold

SPIRITUAL VENTURERS' EDUCATION TRUST
AUCKLAND NEW ZEALAND

ISBN 0 7223 1516-3
Printed in Great Britain by
Arthur H. Stockwell Ltd.
Elms Court   Ilfracombe
Devon

The media today is continually bringing to our attention the subject of Earth changes which are said to lie ahead of the planet. This is added to daily by a great flood of books and articles upon the subject. Such reports tend to be shrugged off as mere fanciful nonsense by the majority, whilst others become deeply fearful of the future. Mankind has always had prophets of doom, ever at hand to warn of death and destruction unless Man repented. From long-gone Biblical times to the modern day, psychics have tried to indicate a path for Mankind. In the main they tend to indicate the end of the world and destruction for the human race.

Whilst within these pages you may find much that will disturb, it is not intended as a prophecy of doom, indeed, it does have a message of light. There is no end in sight for the planet, although there will be some rather drastic changes. In reaching back into my past and linking it with my future, I have endeavoured to illustrate the pattern of life. There is no end, all action sets in motion further action; that which we think and do today, we shall fulfil tomorrow.

Mankind stands on the brink of the most glorious new Age — Aquarius. Within it the race of Man will reach new heights of expression, his civilization will become almost perfect, based as it will be, upon a conscious awareness of his One-ness with the Creator of All Life. What we achieve within that new Age depends completely upon what we do today. Thought is the key — and we may no longer put off until tomorrow that which we know we must do today, unless we wish to reap a bitter harvest.

Chapter 1

I gazed dumbly at the pile of news cuttings scattered about me. When I had asked the Agency to provide me with all news items relating to Earth changes I had scarcely realized that it would open the flood gates to all that which I had so successfully dammed in the recesses of my mind for many years. My mind was in a whirl — it was all happening, just as the Brothers had said it would! The clippings indicated the world changes which apparently were now in daily evidence. Living an hermetically sealed life, I had scarcely noted the reports in my daily papers, yet here, culled from the world's press and magazines, was ample evidence of the destruction of which I had been forewarned so many years ago. Earthquakes, accelerating in their occurrence and ferocity; wars, revolts and strife were becoming the daily order of life world wide. In less detail were reports of the increasing level of changes in the world's weather patterns, the climates appearing to be changing overnight. All without explanation, even the scientists at a loss for the underlying reasons. I returned to the report in my hand, dealing with a horrifying earthquake in Algeria: a 7·5 tremor had caused a devastating loss of life and the region was still being rocked with smaller 'quakes.

As I pondered on the report, my mind went back over the years. What was it my spiritual mentor — Wen Shu — had said? "Vision tomorrow . . . . Gaze at what Man and planet between them will achieve as this current Age sinks into chaos. Vision tomorrow . . . ." Slowly it all began to filter back into my mind and with it came the deep dread that I had put from me for so many years. Those experiences, commencing in my childhood, had years later sounded like the ravings of a madman to those with whom I attempted to share them.

As I sat transfixed, the visions began to sweep over me again like some horrific film which awaited my participation. I was swept up on a wave of fear and nausea as the scenes began to unfold once more in my mind's eye. I hovered over a scene of almost total destruction; all about me terrified people ran for shelter, few finding respite, the majority falling under the hail of bullets. The air was filled with screams of terror and pain; as far as the eye could see was the destruction of the once proud city of Paris, a clear indication that the ruthless onslaught of the forces which came in the name of Mahomet would not rest until they had erased that once fair city from the face of the earth.

The soldiers appeared to be drawn from almost every East European and African State. Hate filled their eyes, for this was no ordinary war — they fought for their belief and death came to all who failed to make obeisance. The destruction was total and more horrifying than any unleashed in the Crusades of the Dark Ages. Without volition I was torn away from that scene and immediately assailed by a spectacle even more devastating. Hovering over the great port of Marseilles, which was scarcely recognizable, for so much havoc had ensued, I saw the remains of many great cargo and warships engulfed in flame and smoke while on the land great tanks rumbled through the smouldering remains of the port, seeking further targets to devastate. A pall of black acrid smoke hung low over the city, little but the tanks moving. An air of desolation filled the atmosphere; the city and its people were almost totally wiped out.

At this stage I pulled myself back to consciousness with a start, my throat dry with fear and the scenes still vivid in my mind. Sweeping the clippings to the floor I staggered over to the typewriter and feverishly inserted a fresh sheet of paper. It was now or never. Yet as I sat poised to start, the words eluded me, emotion still running amok within my being. A literary agent I had spoken to some months ago had shouted excitedly, "Get it down on paper, quickly, before it all happens." Yet I was still filled with reluctance to express openly all that had been shown to me so long ago, for I feared a renewal of the scorn and derision of most, and the deep fear which filled the eyes of old friends whenever I spoke of these things. Had I really the courage to face that situation on a much wider scale? Until today, I had not, yet now I felt urged to set it down. The news clippings gave me the confirmation I needed. Had I the right to refuse to share this vital information? Or not to make others aware in order that the more erudite among them might make some attempt to salvage something for the future race? The questions raced through my mind and as they did so, other memories began to surface.

In my mind I travelled back down the years to those early days of my youth when, as a hypersensitive child, the nightmares and strange dream-like experiences had begun. I was only eight years old when the first visitation occurred and I was shocked into wakefulness by the power of a voice calling through the night "Mneb-Ra . . . Mneb-Ra . . . . Come along, it is time for us to begin."

Rubbing my eyes sleepily I asked "Begin what?" The room was filled with an intense golden light which made observation difficult and I could not see where the voice was coming from. "What time is it?" I said, still not yet fully awake.

"Never mind foolish talk of time," came the rather short reply, "it is time of a different dimension I wish to reveal to you. Come along — we have not much time." As I slowly became accustomed to the light I saw before me a Being clad in a white robe, the face creased with humour at the unintentional pun. In vain I looked for wings, half expecting this dream-like apparition to be the manifestation of an Angelic Being. "No wings," my visitor chuckled, "I do not need them, I can move through time and space in a trice, merely by thinking myself there!"

"Oooh!" I cried, filled with wonderment, "can you teach *me* to do that?"

"Later, my son, later. Now it is time for much more important things," he replied. My childish disappointment must have been apparent for he smiled in a kindly manner and placed an arm around me. "Come," he said, "let us away, we have to continue your training."

Gathered to him, I soon became aware of the terrifying
sensations which I had experienced for some months during
the night. It felt as though I was growing larger, hands and
arms swelling to four or five times their normal size. "No! No!"
I shouted in terror, "not that dream again!"

He held me tightly to him and said soothingly, "Hush my
son, it is not a dream. I am taking you on a journey to a
different world and for that you must leave your earthly body
behind. What you sense and fear is the casting aside of the
physical body, but trust me. Hold tight and you will have
nothing to fear."

Shutting my eyes tightly and swallowing my youthful fears, I
grasped his arm and sank into oblivion. Many times in the
following years my nightly visitor appeared and took me
travelling into the night, but I never remembered where we
went.

The name he called me by was always a puzzle to me. Why
did he not use my proper name, why use that strange one
'Mneb-Ra'? I had often intended to question him on this
matter, but whenever he appeared the questions vanished in
the excitement of the night journeys. Not for many years was I
to become aware of the meaning or portent of that name.
Thankfully, in my tender years, the information was withheld.

As a child I was almost always alone, deep in my thoughts,
unable to mix freely with others of my own age, feeling
awkward and 'different'. Disliking sport, the taunt of 'sissy'
merely tended to increase my solitude and I began to become
introverted. During my formative years I had been deeply
troubled by the fact that I appeared to be occupying a body
that was not mine. I simply could not fathom how I acquired it
or how I came to be in my present situation. There was no one
I could ask, lest I be scolded, and this merely served to
accentuate my feeling of being 'different' or 'odd'. I felt
deprived, wanting desperately to return to that other body,
that other 'time' which I sensed existed, and where I had been
so happy. Try as I might I could not reconcile myself to my
current existence.

In my early teens I found a quiet place where few entered
unless they had sorrowful business to attend to. Hence the local
cemetery became my haven of refuge and peace. Here, I could

day-dream to my heart's content with little fear of being disturbed. Not for one moment did I consider the nature of the setting to be macabre, for since early childhood I had felt that life on Earth was merely a period of expression, and that other 'time' one to which we would all return one day. Death had never held any fear for me as a result.

Sitting deep in thought under my favourite elder tree one afternoon, I was suddenly aware of the now familiar voice of Wen Shu.

"Come, my son, you have spent more than enough time pondering on what might have been. Now it is time to set the record straight and to reveal a little of that upon which you so often contemplate."

He stood before me in the guise which he had long since adopted, that of a genial, white-haired man clad in a long Oriental robe. His shoulders were bent with age, yet he radiated the most intense joy and love and I was caught up in this emanation and longed to run to him and embrace him with great affection.

"Are you taking me on a trip? In day-time?" I asked incredulously.

He laughed softly. "Not that type of journey, my son, but a journey through time, for you must now become acquainted with your past and then your future. There is much for you to absorb." He sat beside me and gazed into my eyes with an expression of deep love as he began to talk.

"Since you were quite young you have had memories which have disturbed you. Memories of another body, another time, and quite often you have wondered why you had your present form. You also carry with you deep memories of Atlantis, to which you have held fast in spite of that which you have been taught in your schoolroom. It is time now to pull aside a little the curtain which holds back the past, in an endeavour to show you something of that which was.

"First, you must realize that time, as such, does not exist; it is something which has been constructed by Man and for Man to indicate his passage through the plane of matter. Secondly, as you are well aware, there is no such thing as death in the accepted sense. The physical body is but a garment adopted for a period of time in order that lessons may be gained within it, also to bring about spiritual growth as the end product of such experience. Nothing around you is real — it is a vast illusion. Later, in your schoolroom, you will learn that matter is composed of atoms, that those atoms vibrate at the same rate as Man, enabling him to see, touch and use them.

"This illusionary world is what is termed the third dimension and one day all must leave it behind. Then it will seem that they have awoken from a long dream. They will find themselves within the fourth dimension — that of spiritual reality. It will seem as solid and as real as that they have recently left behind, yet in the main, it is equally illusionary. Upon the fourth dimension, worlds are created from thought. That which Man cultivates during his lifetime he will inherit upon his departure from the world of matter. It will be his to utilize until he begins to perceive the truth beyond it. Then he will progress to higher levels to absorb the lessons those levels have to teach him.

"Many years ago I told you I did not need wings to fly, that I could project myself through time and space to a different dimension. I am now going to teach you to fly backwards through time." So saying, he stretched out his hands towards me, placed one upon the top of my head and the other upon the centre of my brow; I felt a sharp burning sensation and became extremely light-headed. In addition to this I was aware of bright colours flashing before my eyes.

"Close your eyes my son and simply concentrate upon that which I will show you, the meaning of which I will relate in due course," he said calmly.

I found myself wandering along a dark woodland path, surrounded on all sides by gigantic trees which dwarfed me. The air was dank and thick ferns and mosses grew in great abundance. All about me was semi-darkness, yet I had no fear as I sped along the path and I was able to sense my direction quite easily. As I gazed down at my body I was surprised to note the form of a woman who appeared to be in her late thirties, clothed in a simple, short white robe, roughly made from a flaxen material. Dark hair hung low below the shoulders of a lithe athletic body which had a reddish-brown tinge to the skin. Over all I appeared to be some seven feet tall. My loping tread soon took me into a clearing where a number of men and women were gathered, some occupied in weaving flax, but the majority merely sitting watching in bored idleness.

My entry into the clearing evoked interest from one or two of the flax weavers, who waved or acknowledged my presence; although no voices were heard I was aware of the greeting and returned their greeting in a similarly silent manner, making my way purposefully towards the back of the clearing, above which a mighty rock towered majestically. Throwing myself upon the earth at the base of the rock I rested whilst awaiting some further form of mental communication. After a time I rose and moved towards a small stream which dissected the clearing from east to west. Discarding the robe I immersed my body in its chilling waters, thoroughly enjoying its refreshing energies and on emerging, shook myself dry rather in the fashion of a wild dog and donned the robe once more. Thoroughly refreshed I then returned to the base of the rock, where I sought out a deep cleft, within which I located a small bundle of dry twigs and carrying this beneath one arm, proceeded to swarm up the face of the rock rather like an agile mountain goat.

Once at the top I stopped to regain my breath. Before me stood a lofty figure clad in a long white flaxen robe; his back was towards me, his arms stretched heavenwards in an attitude of supplication.

Slowly he turned towards me and the kindly features of Wen Shu held my gaze. He held out his hands and I gave him the bundle of twigs which he set upon a near-by flat-topped rock, urging me to kneel as he did so. I knelt down, gazing at him in silent awe as he resumed his soundless invocation to the Cosmic Source of All Light. After a while he turned, and with an impassive air struck the bundle of twigs with his right hand; within moments a small tongue of flame arose, setting light to the bundle of twigs. With one hand upon his heart, he extended towards me with the other the now steadily burning torch and with my right hand symbolically upon my heart I accepted it as I knelt before him, then rising and inclining my head reverently in his direction I began to descend the rock face with the same uncaring agility with which I had ascended it.

Landing in the clearing once more, I silently and purposefully made my way through the throng of startled onlookers and took the path I had so recently trod. Before long I approached yet another clearing where others were gathered awaiting my coming. On reaching the centre of this clearing I stopped before a small rock upon which were many twigs; placing the burning torch to them I ignited what was a ceremonial fire and the male guardian saluted, placing one hand upon his heart and bowing low. My task completed, I left the clearing and moved swiftly back down the woodland path.

Chapter 2

At this point, the vision faded and I was once more in my familiar churchyard with Wen Shu close by my side. I gazed at him in startled amazement. "Where was I? Why was I in that body? What was the meaning of it?" The questions tumbled from my lips as I sought to understand all that I had witnessed and felt.

Wen Shu was rather amused at my eager haste and replied, "One at a time my son, one at a time. Did I not tell you that I would relate the happenings? Calm yourself first, then listen."

I drew a deep breath and then another, thereby obtaining a measure of calm, although my mind still seethed with questions held in abeyance.

Wen Shu continued . . . . "This was your first meaningful lifetime in the continent of Atlantis, and the planet still being in a primeval state, life was experienced in a vastly different manner than that to which you are accustomed today. You chose for that lifetime to experiment with the female form and incarnated with the Tlavatly race. These were a mountain-loving people who settled temporarily upon the western coastal regions of the continent before moving into the mountainous regions at a later date.

"During this lifetime you acquired the greatly sought after role of Fire-Bringer. This responsibility was awarded to you as the result of much earlier life experiences during which you proved to be a willing servant of Sanat Kumara. During the life envisaged, you carried the Sacred Flame from settlement to settlement, according to instructions received from the Planetary Logos."

Unable to contain my curiosity any longer I rudely interrupted his explanations. "But *you* were there! . . . ." Unperturbed by this interruption he continued.

"Of course, my son; it was but one of several lifetimes in which we have linked together. Others will be revealed at a later time."

"What is a 'Planetary Logos' and who is 'Sanat Kumara'?" I again interrupted, eager to extend my knowledge.

"They are different names for the same Force," he replied patiently. "The Planetary Logos, whom we also know as Sanat Kumara, incarnated within the body of the planet during the Lemurian epoch in order that the evolution of the planet might be speeded up." Gazing at me in a benign fashion he forestalled my next question. "Lemuria was a continent which preceded Atlantis and you did not incarnate within that time, therefore it does not concern you."

Returning to his explanation he continued: "Sanat Kumara oversees all growth upon the planet and in the early days of the Atlantean continent all who wished to aid this growth served under Sanat Kumara, helping him to bring to fruition the Cosmic Plan for Earth. During those early days, long before the life you have just envisioned, those incarnating into human form assisted the Devic kingdom with the formation of soils. The Devas are those whom today you jokingly refer to as gnomes, elves and fairies. They are Nature's elementals and come directly under the control of Sanat Kumara.

"All at that point in time utilized to the full their psychic powers, fully realizing the need for continued growth upon every level of experience. There was no strife, such as exists today upon Earth."

"Why did I take fire to the different settlements? Could they not make their own?" I queried, a little nonplussed by my role.

He smiled at me and answered, "Fire, at that point in time — and for some considerable time after — was strictly guarded and controlled. Man looked upon it as a gift of the Gods. As so many still lived in primeval darkness in the midst of the forests, the taking of light to the different settlements was a symbolic act. Only special souls were allowed to hold the role of Fire-Bringer and during the life in question you were more than content with your function, never seeking a mate, knowing full well that your soul-mate was not incarnate. You must try to understand that the renewal of the race at that time was also strictly controlled, mating being at the specific direction of priests and not otherwise.

"This for you was not a long lifetime, for during that period all were allowed to vacate the physical form once they had developed the vehicle as far as they could. They then returned to the higher realms to contemplate their next action in accordance with Cosmic Law. In this they had to act in unison with the Overself, of course, which in turn co-operates with the Group Soul and the Lords of Karma."

I gazed at him in perplexed awe. "Who . . . what . . . are they?" I whispered.

He patted the seat beside him and bade me sit, while he explained. "The Overself is your real self, of which you, as you know yourself, are but a tiny fragment of its consciousness. In itself, the Overself is a minute portion of that Being which you call God. Therefore that spiritual energy within your physical form which energizes and directs it, is Divine in essence. Within the Overself you have all knowledge, of all that is, and ever will be. What it lacks is experience, and incarnation into the worlds of matter brings that vitally necessary experience and hopefully, a return to your Divine source as bliss consciousness, having experienced all things — and most importantly — having overcome the pull of matter."

I pondered upon this strange new knowledge, unable fully to grasp his meaning, but anxious to seek answers to all that he spoke of. "What exactly do you mean by a Group Soul?" I asked tentatively.

"It is the eternal group to which you will belong until all within it reach the same stage of self-mastery," he replied. "None may progress beyond the group itself, all must aid the others. Those who determinedly lag behind and hold up the progress must be assisted, great effort often being necessary to aid the tardy of spirit. You will meet members of that group as you progress through this lifetime. It will be the meeting or reunion of souls. They are special people to whom you will be drawn — strangers, yet very familiar to you — and they will have a great part to play in your destiny and you in turn in theirs."

"You spoke also of the Lords of Karma. Who are they?" I asked.

Placing his arm around my shoulders he continued with his explanation. "The Lords of Karma can perhaps be likened to your Parliament upon Earth. To them falls the task of noting all transgressions of the Divine Law and the subsequent allocation of situations within which all might find the opportunity for a just repayment. It is the Law of Sequence and Consequence and is ever fair. There are many in your world who feel encouraged to do just as they wish, taking to themselves that which satisfies their appetites regardless of the cost to others. Such souls will have to learn that in doing so they transgress Cosmic Law and eventually they must repay, in full. It is the abuse of the Divine gift of free will which makes the constant return to the worlds of matter necessary. Those who abuse the God-given gift must learn — often through bitter experience — that they may not ride rough-shod over their brother Man."

Gazing at me intently and noting my deep interest, he continued. "There is an overwhelming need for all to understand and accept the necessity for the true brotherhood of Man, regardless of colour or creed. It is particularly vital at this present time on your Earth plane. Sadly, Man still has a long way to go towards this goal." Pausing to pat my shoulder fondly he said, "Here I must take my leave of you, my son. Study well that which you have seen and heard. Absorb it well, for at a later point in time you will require this knowledge."

He began to fade from view almost as quickly as he had appeared and I was left to mull over the strange happenings of the day.

Chapter 3

As I came back to a state of consciousness with a start, a glance
at the clock told me that my reverie had lasted for more than
an hour. "This will not do," I muttered to myself. "If I am
going to get this down I cannot spend hours day-dreaming."

Shaking my head in an attempt to clear it I began to gather
up the scattered clippings. As I did so my eyes fell upon an
article which I had overlooked. A dramatic headline had
caught my eyes, which read: 'Hold on to your seats for 1981!'
In it, a psychic gave a series of predictions for greatly increased
activity in the occurrence of earthquakes world wide and went
on to paint a rather grim picture for the race of Man over all. I
caught my breath. Some of that which I read I could not relate
to, yet in the back of my mind cogs were clicking into place.
Something, somewhere in the past, was beginning to surface.
Parts of the report were very familiar. "What was it?" I mused
aloud, as I paced back and forth. Something the Brothers had
told me, years ago.

Sitting down, I willed the elusive pattern to emerge from the
depths of my mind. The memory slowly began to float in hazily
and as I closed my eyes in an endeavour to clarify the memory
pattern, it began to crystallize . . . .

I had been meditating when the Teachers had approached
me for the first time on the conscious level. Some of them were
familiar to me, for I had studied with them in the Halls of
Learning during my sleep state. They had about them an air
of purpose which was a little unsettling and as I pondered on
what it might be, Wen Shu's voice interrupted my reverie.

"There is no cause for alarm, my son, although you are
correct in your assumption. The Brothers are gathered here
that they might lend their energies to the task ahead of us. As
you are aware each of them has knowledge in specific fields
and will lend their aid where necessary."

"What is so important that they join me at this time?" I
asked a little apprehensively, my curiosity aroused.

At this point I intercepted a thought pattern from the
Atlantean Teacher whose face was grave with purpose, as ever.
"You must now become aware of that which lies ahead in your
tomorrow."

I felt a familiar feeling of dread. If they intended to reveal more destruction I was not at all sure that I wished to participate. Hesitantly I asked, "What is it that you wish me to do?" at the same time realizing that my wishes did not really enter into the matter at all.

He held my gaze as he replied: "You must first realize that much of that which we reveal need not necessarily affect the race of Man in the manner indicated. Within a measure, Mankind has the ability to circumvent the greater calamaties. Even if the race as a whole is not able to achieve that, they may certainly lessen the effects of certain happenings."

"How?" I asked rather bluntly.

"Through the correct and positive use of their thought patterns. Every situation which in the past has brought about the downfall of Man and his civilization has been caused by the destructive use of thought patterns," was his grim rejoinder.

I turned this over in my mind. "How may a few, using their thought patterns positively, overcome the force released by the many who use their thought patterns destructively?" I asked.

Here Wen Shu swiftly intervened with, "The few must learn to encourage the correct use of thought upon all levels during their daily lives. We do not say that this will be a simple task, but it is one which can be achieved with determination. In this you will continue the work you commenced long ago as Mneb-Ra. During that time you were fully aware that the only hope for the race lay in the instruction of your people in the correct use of their thought. Now you will have the opportunity to achieve that long-forgotten goal."

"We must now proceed," broke in the Atlantean, with a hint of impatience. "Let us first advise you of that which lies ahead and then we shall instruct you in the matter of visioning."

"I am ready," I replied, although in fact, my head was spinning.

He gazed at me rather quizzically, but as I made no response, he continued. "First you must realize that the race of Man is not expected to undergo tests of the magnitude which face him in the decades ahead without positive assistance. The Creator always provides the wherewithal to enable even the weakest to accomplish the seemingly impossible. It will be so now."

"What exactly do you mean by 'wherewithal'?" I questioned.

Almost as though he anticipated this question the answer

came at once. "I refer to energies of an exceptionally powerful nature which will be unleashed upon the planet, with the sole aim of stimulating the higher consciousness of the race of Man."

"How will we know those energies? Will we be able to see them?" I asked somewhat ingenuously.

He gave one of his rare smiles. "Can you see electrical energy?"

Somewhat abashed, I muttered, "No, I cannot — but you say I am to share this knowledge; therefore I must know, for many will ask the same question. How will they know?"

Wen Shu, sensing my frustration, interrupted. "Their consciousness will change my son. Those who search for truth will find it. Their awareness of Cosmic matters will expand and in turn they must become the instructors of their spiritually blind brothers."

"When will that occur?" I asked eagerly.

"Time is irrelevant my son, but these things will take place during the last quarter of your current century."

I was suddenly caught up in the inevitability of it all, my mind upon those closest to me. "What of those who are not spiritually aware — what happens to them?" I muttered anxiously.

The Atlantean leaned forward and answered, "Over a period of eighteen months of your Earth time, great planetary forces will be brought to bear upon the Earth plane. These forces will have the effect of intensifying the thought patterns of Man. Those who obstinately refuse to lift their thoughts above mundane and materialistic matters will, in effect, become doubly negative and great efforts will then have to be made to rescue them from their self-created collision with reality."

I gazed at him uncomprehendingly. "I am not at all sure of your meaning," I said.

Patiently he replied. "For those who are determined to remain locked within the illusionary world of matter, only the destruction of that world of illusion will awaken them to the reality."

I looked at him in dawning horror. "Is that what is meant by 'the end of the world'?" I asked.

Wen Shu smiled at me, a wealth of compassion within his smile, then gently chided me. "No, no, my son, the planet has much that it must accomplish before that day comes. We refer only to the termination of current civilizations."

"Do you mean that they will be destroyed in much the same manner as the Atlantean civilization?" I asked, still somewhat fearfully.

"In a manner of speaking you can surmise that, my son. There were, of course, other great civilizations prior to that one, which also outgrew themselves."

"Then what hope is there for the race of Man if his civilization is to fall?" I queried, confused and unable to grasp the full portent of what was being said. "Will life go on? And if so — how?"

Here, the Atlantean leaned forward and spoke. "There will always be what can be termed 'safe places' upon the planet where the spiritually aware among the human race will be encouraged to flee and these will provide the nucleus of the new race which will move forward into the new Golden Age which will then unfold upon the planet. Do not become bogged down in the destruction. After all — you are well aware that there is no death. Those who must encounter suffering or lose their life during this period have chosen this path, for it will bring them to a point of inner illumination not possible in many mundane incarnations in the world of matter."

I thought about this for a while. "You speak of a new race. Is this why there are members of every race located upon all continents today? Will the new race be formed out of them — or their survivors?" I finally asked.

"Those among them who are prepared to develop their insight and follow the plan which will be revealed to them — yes . . . . That is what is intended," the Atlantean answered.

A new thought struck me. "You said there would be 'safe places' — where are they?"

At this outburst, Wen Shu smiled gently. "You will be shown your point of safety my son; do not attempt to place yourself at a point where you are not meant to be."

Somewhat crestfallen by this comment, and feeling rather sheepish, I could not help thinking, 'I would be safe — but how?' However, there had been hope for me in the answer and with that I had to be content. Gazing at Wen Shu I said, "Others will be bound to ask me the same question. If I am to forewarn, should I not know where the safe places are?"

One of the Brothers who had until this time remained silent, then intervened. "We agree, but we cannot provide specifics at this point in time, for Man will have to earn the right to safety. However, it may be sufficient for you to indicate the general area of the safe places." Looking at me intently, he continued. "One such place will be located in Northern Europe at a point where the Great Bear holds many in physical bondage. However, the spirit cannot be so repressed and the people will rise against their oppressors, bringing to an end the reign of tyranny."

My Atlantean friend placed his hands upon my shoulders. "In the South Pacific, a fertile paradise will link with a nigh-barren neighbour and together with new lands which will rise from the sea bed, will form a great point of strength for the new Age. This will only come about once they have learned to throw off the materialistic yoke. Again, in the North Americas, where the Shield is strong, peace will be found; finally, in the Central Americas, where much of an ancient civilization lies undisturbed, a further point of safety will be located."

I sat quietly, digesting that which had been revealed. "It is a little vague," I finally ventured.

Wen Shu smiled broadly. "It will become clear at the correct time, my son. We would not wish to encourage a mass influx of power-seekers to points of spiritual outgrowth."

Seeing the wisdom in his words I acknowledged this with a smile and a nod of the head, holding back the other questions on that subject which still clamoured for an answer in my mind.

"How will the changes begin?" I eventually asked, anxious now to proceed.

The Atlantean rose and paced the floor before he replied. "They will begin with the partial collapse of the bed of the great ocean adjacent to the continent you know as India. This in turn will create a series of tidal waves which will then strike the coastal regions of that land, laying waste much of it. The waves themselves will exceed two hundred feet in height and little will survive the impact."

Aghast, I cried, "What will bring about this collapse of the ocean floor, then?"

"The crust of the planet is extremely volatile at that point and there will be a need for the pressures built up beneath the surface to find release. This will in turn set in motion many other eruptions," was his answer.

"Where will they occur?" I interrupted, unable now to contain my curiosity.

"The lands of the Samurai will undergo great change," he replied. "A great deal of that land will sink beneath the waves." I gasped aloud at this, but held my tongue. He continued: "The great Ring of Fire will then burst into life, bringing in its wake the collapse of the bed of the ocean adjacent to the Boot of the Mediterranean, causing the great fire mount there to spew forth destruction."

I waited in tense silence, unable to comment, my mind in a whirl at these revelations.

Wen Shu took up the narrative. "Along the Ring of Fire the destructive energies will speed until the polarity shall be found in its sister, deep within the islands of the Spanish Main. Fire will rain down, destroying all before it."

"Will that then be the end of the destruction?" I asked hopefully.

"Merely the beginning," was the grim rejoinder. "Within months the western coastlands of the Americas will undergo upheaval as the earth shakes and fire is cast high into the air. The coastlines will then begin to alter their shape."

"Is there more?" I whispered tremulously.

"Not at that time," he said. "However, earth changes will increase in their intensity. Man has foolishly ignored many earlier warnings and builds upon the points where the great discs meet beneath the surface. Great cities will topple as Mammon is overthrown."

"What cities?" I asked apprehensively.

"Those that are built alongside the great fissures where the land heaves and falls in an effort to release the pressures building beneath its surface," came the reply.

"You appear to refer only to the North Americas — is all

else safe?" I asked.

"For a time," replied the Atlantean, "but with the inundation of the city where the gate of Collossus stands, powerful forces will then be unleashed upon the lands where the Shield is strong, opening wide the fault within its waterway. A gigantic wave will then bring destruction to all the cities built alongside it and extensive flooding to large areas adjacent to inland waters. In like manner the great waves will spread across the vast ocean until they dash themselves upon the lands of the north."

"England! — do you mean England?" I cried in fear.

He studied my face, his features serious. "This land and others adjacent must feel the lash of Neptune's tail." Noting my fear he continued: "The peoples of the northern lands shall have two years in which to seek safety, following which the changes will begin in earnest."

This news simply shattered me and I could no longer hold on to the meditative state. The Brothers began to fade from view and I was left to contemplate the future.

My mind reeled under the onslaught of so many thoughts as they vied with each other for attention. Most insistent was the thought — what of my family, my home, my friends? I must warn them! At this juncture I became aware of Wen Shu's presence; his thought pattern impressed itself upon my mind.

"As with all others, my son, they will be given the opportunity to choose. Your earthly family, in common with all members of the human family of Man, have many lessons to absorb this time round. You cannot know where their destiny lies and it would not be correct for you to be made aware of it. Set the example: share the truth and allow them to decide for themselves."

Suitably chastened, I was then left to contemplate the happenings of a very startling and disturbing day.

Chapter 4

The ringing of the telephone brought me back to the present with a severe jolt. I gazed at the instrument uncomprehendingly for some moments, for the recent experience had been so real that I found great difficulty in reorientating myself. Deciding that I was not in a fit state to talk to anyone upon everyday matters, I let it ring, knowing that sooner or later the caller would tire in the attempt. Thoughts whirling round and round in my head soon blocked the strident tones of the telephone and for me it ceased to exist. The mention by Wen Shu of a task I had begun in Atlantis and which awaited completion in this life, triggered off other memories of that long-gone continent.

In my mind's eye a long-forgotten scene began to emerge. I was once more sitting in my spot under the elder tree in the churchyard, expectantly awaiting the arrival of my spirit mentor. Earlier, a voice had instructed me to make my way there, as there were further revelations awaiting me. As I waited, I wondered what the reaction of a mourner would be if he chanced upon my meeting with a strangely-garbed Oriental gentleman! At that time it did not occur to me that no one other than myself could perceive my visitor — unless they too happened to be clairvoyant and on the same wavelength, which was most unlikely.

The arrival of Wen Shu interrupted this chain of thought. He placed his arm around my shoulders, saying, "Come my son, it is time to pick up once more the threads of your past and to continue our journey through time." He again placed his hands upon the crown of my head and upon my brow, bringing once more the burning sensation, together with the odd, light-headed feeling. As these subsided I found myself within a small, single-storeyed building constructed from a white stone which gave off a glow. There was no visible means of illumination, yet the whole was brilliantly lit. As I moved about, I noticed that my skin was a deep copper hue and that I wore a strange white robe which fell to the floor.

I moved silently into an inner chamber and began to disrobe, exchanging the long white garment for a short blue robe and added a pair of rope-soled sandals to my feet. This completed, I returned to the main room, gathered a number of neatly-bound bundles from a small pile of brushwood and took them into a small antechamber where there was an upright stone of the same composition as the walls of the building. Upon it stood a blue oblong container of a substance similar to alabaster; on lifting the upper portion of this, a small flame within was revealed and this flared suddenly as the inrush of air met it. From this I ignited one of the bundles of brushwood and swiftly left the building.

Setting off at a steady jog-trot I was a little amazed at how speedily I covered the ground. Gazing about me, I judged my height to be some seven feet, which made my task an easy one. Following a trail through the undergrowth I made steadily towards a hill on the horizon and once there, it was possible to see a small settlement, deep in the valley. Continuing my steady pace I reached this just as the light of day was beginning to fade on the horizon. As I reached the perimeter of the settlement a cry could be heard within — "The Fire Guardian! The Fire Guardian!" Soon I was surrounded by a small group of men who kept a respectful distance from me; there were no women or children to be seen.

Entering the square in the midst of the settlement I handed the now fading torch to a village elder, first igniting one of my remaining torches from it. "No bonfires this time Old One, or else I will suspend your supply of the flame for a month," I said sternly.

The elder fell to his knees, clutching the torch to him. "Oh please Guardian, not that, please do not suspend the flame. I promise I will ensure that it is used correctly," he cried.

"See that you do, then, for the flame must not be abused. Use it only for culinary purposes. There is no need to light bonfires — the animals will not attack unless you abuse them in some manner." So saying I turned about and sped off into the night on my errand of light.

As if in a dream I watched my behaviour in some amazement, for I appeared to hold the same role of authority and once again it was related to the distribution of fire. Unlike my earlier experiences, the people were not dwelling in the midst of the forests, as there appeared to be some definite form of settled life and civilization, but this still seemed to depend upon the distribution of fire for culinary purposes, and I also noted that it was not used to light or heat their homes.

My reverie was interrupted by the voice of my mentor. "That which you have seen took place at the beginning of the third epoch of the Atlantean civilization. You bypassed the second epoch, having a preference for sun and warmth. Again you chose the element of fire as your means of service to the race. By this time it was under very strict surveillance with rigid rules pertaining to its use and special guardians were appointed to watch over it day and night, issuing suitable quantities to the populace at their discretion. Bonfires were not permitted, although there were many fearful of the large animals which roamed the face of the planet. This had not always been the case, for the animal kingdom had once lived in harmony with Man in accordance with the laws of Sanat Kumara. Sadly, some misguided members of the human race began to mate with animals for sport and this brought hideous malformed creatures into being. From that point on, the animal kingdom began to attack its tormentors.

"The role of Fire Guardian for a district was a very responsible office and one which you had to work hard to attain. It required a fairly long apprenticeship and you did not attain your own fire-cell until late in that life. During that lifetime you utilized your mediumistic abilities to forewarn the people of impending disasters which lay ahead of them, for this period was not far distant from the time of a major cataclysm which rent the continent apart. You opted out of that physical form late in your thirties, feeling that you had accomplished as much as you could with that particular form."

As I returned to consciousness and my seat under the elder tree, my mind was buzzing. It was so very difficult to imagine a time when fire was rationed in such a manner and the people disciplined in the way I had seen.

"What lesson did I learn from that lifetime?" I asked Wen Shu.

He smiled. "Later in this life you will see the purpose in revealing that portion of your past to you. A similar role awaits you in which again you must bring light to Man and forewarn those who will listen of impending changes. The past repeats itself."

Chapter 5

My mind raced backwards over the many times I had met with Wen Shu and the wealth of knowledge he had imparted to me. I would always remember the time he chose to make a rather startling appearance in order to teach me the fields of energy. I had been sitting lost in a dream world when I became aware of a field of energy building up in the midst of the room. Commencing at floor level, a bright force-field gradually built up until it finally took the shape of my beloved mentor. He turned slowly, allowing me to observe every intricate pattern of his gown, before stepping forward to embrace me, his face beaming with love.

"You startled me — you have never appeared in that fashion before!" I gasped, most intrigued as I awaited his explanation of his unusual manner of manifestation.

He chuckled, then said, "I wished you to understand a little more about the field of energy, my son, as my world is composed of pure energy and we merely adapt it to our use. This method of projection into the third dimension is not so unusual — one day all Mankind must learn to adapt to such energy and acquire awareness on how they might dwell within it, yet still be part of the plane of matter. Still — that subject is for a later time. I feel that you have had sufficient time to mull over the events of our last meeting. Besides, we have been rather busy in the astral worlds of late."

Here I interrupted with: "Why is it that I cannot remember where I have been during the sleep state? There appears to be little point to such exercises if I cannot bring memory back into the conscious state."

Patting my arm he answered, "That is your task my son. You must instruct your conscious mind that it must tap into the sleep-state happenings in order that you might have memory."

I gazed at him incredulously: "And how do I achieve that, I'd like to know?"

Ignoring my tone of voice, he continued: "Before sinking into the sleep state, instruct the conscious mind that it is to bring back memory of where you have been during your sleep travels. It will take a little time to perfect, but it will come about eventually. The mind must do that which you instruct it to accomplish. Keep a notebook beside your bed, for often you will awake in the middle of the night and must note down at that time the memories you have. They will fade by morning."

"That sounds very easy!" I answered with enthusiasm, "I will start this evening."

Again he smiled. "It will not be so simple a task as you may imagine, for you may well resent being awoken in the early hours of the morning. You will have to discipline the self to take notes. However, do try, for it is a very positive manner in which to obtain the information you seek."

I soon found that Wen Shu's directive was not so simple to follow. Morning after morning I awoke to a blank pad — and a blank mind! Feeling rather down-hearted, I began to doubt that I would ever remember, but decided to persevere until I had achieved something. This had its reward, for after a while I found that I was able to retain memory of returning to the body, choosing strange and wonderful means of returning to consciousness in time to hear the morning alarum call. But alas, still not conscious recollection of what I had been doing.

One evening as I settled down to sleep, I felt myself lift from the body and begin to float gently towards the ceiling. From that vantage point I was able to look down at my recumbent body. The experience was so very vivid that I pinched myself to discover whether I was asleep or not — and plunged back into my body and a state of wakefulness! Deeply puzzled by this experience, I lay for some time pondering, until my attention was caught by an iridescent glow in the far corner of the room. It was shapeless, but emitted a pulsating energy. Feeling that I was being drawn into this, I ceased to wonder and allowed myself to float into a dream-like state, yet still retaining consciousness of where I was. I soon became aware of a deep buzzing sound and the sensation of flying around the room at an amazing speed. Again I was aware of my body upon the bed and the odd sound appeared to be created by my other self as it flew around the room. Suddenly I was transported to a different scene within which stood Wen Shu, waiting for me.

"You see, my son, it is possible to leave the physical body and still retain conscious awareness of that which you do! Now

— come, we must proceed with the evening's labours."

Soon the scene changed yet again and I was within a strange building, which appeared to be solid, yet it was possible to see through the very walls themselves. A great number of rather distressed people of all races were gathered within this building, in the midst of which was a very efficient matron-like woman busily issuing orders to all and sundry. Those gathered around her seemed so deeply confused that they accepted her directives without question, although they appeared to understand little else.

"Where are we?" I asked my mentor, deeply puzzled.

"This is one of the receiving stations my son, wherein we must begin the reorientation process for these souls, who have recently departed life on the third dimension without the knowledge that there is no death, so many of them are not aware of the fact that they have undergone death on the physical level and do not understand where they are. This is where you will begin to serve during your sleep state. Whilst you still retain an earthly body, you will be accepted by such souls as these. Your task will be to arrange for them to 'settle in', as it were."

I turned to him uncomprehendingly. "How do I fulfil that task? They all seem so lost."

"Indeed they *are* lost, rather like children, totally bewildered by the current happenings. Stand for a time and observe what is said and done by the rather formidable lady in the middle. You will have to pacify them and help them to begin to accept the fact that there is no cessation of life, as they had thought, then encourage them to leave this place with their loved ones, who are anxiously standing by eager to assist as soon as realization comes to them. I will now leave you for a time . . . ." With that he vanished from view and I was left to observe and consider the best way to deal with the very strange happenings around me.

Drawing close to the milling throng, I soon found myself drawn into the activity as bewildered men and women grasped me by the arm and begged me to explain. Some who approached were confused to find that they had full use of their bodies, even limbs which for so long they had learned to live without on the Earth plane. The evening sped by as I endeavoured to explain their current circumstances, until I was aware of a thought pattern instructing me to return to my physical form. As I turned to go, one determined man grabbed my arm.

"'Ere, where you goin'?" he cried frantically.

Trying in vain to free myself from his clutching hands I shouted desperately, "It's time for me to go back . . . ."

"Go back? Go back where?" he demanded, clutching me even tighter.

"Why — back to Earth . . . . It's . . . ."

He interrupted my frantic explanation, his eyes bulging with fear: "Ain't this Earth? Then where the 'ell are we?" he shouted in consternation.

I cast desperately about for help, but even the formidable matron appeared to have vanished. With a great effort I broke his grip and ran as fast as I could for a bus I spied just outside the door. Jumping on, I collapsed, only to find that the man had run after me, determined not to be shaken off, and had leapt on board with an amazing burst of speed. I frenziedly thought of my body and immediately awoke in my bed with vivid memories of the tussle. I lay wondering what had happened to the man as daylight shone through a chink in my bedroom curtains.

From that point on I began to return to the waking state with full memory of what I had been undertaking during the astral-state journeys. Often I was met by a soul I knew as Red Eagle, who would accompany me into the darker levels, first to observe and then later to serve. These levels were rather unpleasant, for unlike the higher planes, there was no colour and no music — indeed, there was little light. All appeared dank and there was always an unpleasant odour. Red Eagle told me that these levels were the thought planes, hells created by those who dwelt there. They could leave at any time they wished, of course — they only had to accept the light we endeavoured to bring and to accept responsibility for their past actions.

Few of the inhabitants of these levels wished to move from their present environment and would often seek to attack me. At first this caused me to fear, until I was taught consciously to project myself back to my earth form at such times, where I was free from attack and could return to my labours on the dark planes at a later point in time.

One evening I found myself in what appeared to be a gigantic tunnel which stretched for what seemed to be miles. This was extremely dark, with many hidden rocks and pitfalls within it. Struggling on the upward incline were many hundreds of people of all races, mainly aged. Some collapsed, crying out in fear that they could go no further. To these I had to give support, encouraging them to rest awhile before continuing on their journey. No matter how they despaired, some force drew them on and none attempted to return whence they had come. It later transpired that this was yet another state of mind, a thought form created by those trapped within it. These were the souls seeking to free themselves from their physical forms, undergoing the death throes and needing assistance to attain the resting station on the plane of light.

Often my task was to take these lost souls to the Garden of Remembrance — a beautiful spot not unlike certain areas of the Earth plane. Here, in gentle woodland settings filled with flowers of every hue and streams which rippled by, they were given assistance by their Earth-family links who had preceded them, and were encouraged to relive their most recent Earth-life. This was vital, for here they had to commit to memory all that which had transpired during that Earthly sojourn. It was often made all the more difficult by the thought patterns of grief emanating from those left behind on the Earth plane who could not come to terms with their recent loss. Such thought patterns awakened these souls, who then tried to return to Earth in an endeavour to assuage the grief, invariably without success. Such grief was often little more than self-pity, for they had not stopped to think that those whom they professed to love had earned the right to leave behind for a time the Earth plane — a place which I was coming to understand was the nearest Man could get to the place he terms Hell.

At a later time, once the memories had been committed to the records, they would have to be taken to a further point of review. Here, with encouragement from their loved ones, they would have to study the blueprint they had created for their most recent Earth experience before they incarnated. Armed with this information they would then have the task of judging that which they had achieved. I was shown time after time that there was no sterner judge than the self. A consolation to many was the fact that they did not have to face a great hall of judgement, something which many of them had feared.

There were other times when I was given a respite from the labours in the resting stations and dark planes. On such nights I would be taken to the Halls of Learning and here I would sit with the Teachers in what appeared to be small Grecian temples constructed from a glowing stone. A small group would sit and discuss any subject on which knowledge was required and I was also given a great deal of insight into matters which I was told would be required later in my current lifetime. Following such experiences I would often walk with Wen Shu and discuss that which I had heard, usually gaining a deeper insight through these discussions.

Chapter 6

For some weeks I stole every available moment I could, to set down all that I could remember. So much had been shown to me over the years and it was difficult to differentiate between that which I had been told and that which I had come to know. Also, the past and the future were a confused mixture in my mind; trying to untangle them proved to be a labour needing much time and effort. As the weeks passed it became easier to bring to the surface the memories I had buried deep for so long within my consciousness — and with them came the many fears which were buried with them.

News reports tended to trigger off the release of these long-forgotten items, often with terrifying results. Engrossed in a report on a possible collision with the earth by a meteorite, I found myself transported into the past, to a point where for a sombre purpose the Brothers had joined me in my meditation.

Seating themselves in a semicircle around me, the Atlantean

spoke first: "So far we have discussed with you some of the happenings which lie ahead. Now, however, we wish you to experience the situations for yourself in order that you may commit them more readily to memory. Through such an experience you will understand more clearly the role you must undertake in this lifetime."

I gazed at him nervously: "What is it you wish me to do?"

He glanced pensively at me before replying. "Today, we wish you to envision the future."

I stared at him in astonishment, for it was one thing to be taken back into one's past, but the future — how could this be?

Without bothering to wait for the question to be voiced, he answered my thought pattern: "Time does not exist, therefore no difficulties will be encountered. Yesterday, today and tomorrow, as you understand them, are all here — everything is in the NOW. We wish you to relax completely and to endeavour to project the spirit self through the Crown Chakra — this will ensure that you retain conscious awareness of your journeyings."

I closed my eyes and focused all my energies upon the projection of the reality out through the top of my head. It turned out to be far easier than I had anticipated.

"Now," he cried: "use your thought patterns as you have learned to do in your astral journeys. Follow me." He then appeared to vanish from sight. All about me was thick mist and I was aware of a high-pitched buzz, rather like the sound of an angry bee. It was some time before I realized that the sound was created as I flew through time and space.

As the mists began to clear I became aware of great glass-fronted buildings which towered above the land all around me. As I got my bearings, the familiar skyline struck a chord within my memory. New York — I was over New York! Every boy wants to journey to that magical place and I gazed in awe at the city of my dreams. Something, however, was amiss: great portions of the city seemed to be under water and the city itself appeared to have been broken by a giant hand. The lower part of Manhattan Island particularly looked as if it had undergone great upheavals and many of the once impressive buildings were little more than twisted rubble.

I gazed sorrowfully at the desolation, finally catching the

sad sight of Liberty where she lay on her side, partially submerged by the waves. Great panic was spreading through the city, bringing to the surface the worst elements of human nature. Many foraged for what they could in the rubble, but apparently there was a desperate food shortage no doubt due to the floods which followed the upheaval, and the law of the jungle stalked the face of this land which was once in the forefront of technological advancement and a land of plenty. Like packs of rabid dogs, men prowled the city streets, taking whatever they wished regardless of the needs of others, impervious to the cries of the trapped and the hungry.

Grasping my arm, the Atlantean directed my gaze out to sea, where a gigantic wave was proceeding northward at a terrifying rate. It towered some two hundred feet above the surface, picking up huge ocean-going vessels and tossing them aside like matchwood. Up the eastern coast it raced, decimating cities as it passed. I watched in horrified fascination, for the wave itself seemed to draw the coastal waters into it as it passed, leaving boats stranded high and dry and then with a stupendous roar releasing them to crash down upon the shoreline with tremendous fury.

"Come," he said: "it is time now to visit the land where the Shield is strong." Swiftly we passed over the wave and made towards the St. Lawrence Seaway. As we reached it, a smaller wave, no less terrifying in its destructiveness, was travelling swiftly down the great waterway. As the wave moved onwards, a great rending was audible and the Seaway seemed momentarily to part, empty, and then fill again with angry waters. The Seaway now appeared to be much wider than it had been before.

I gazed anxiously at my instructor: "What has happened?"

Drawing me to him he shouted above the roar of the seething waters: "The waters have activated a major fault line and the waterway has indeed greatly widened, aided of course by the rapid increase of water levels. Look . . . ." He pointed to a picturesque city which even now was being battered by the waves. "Quebec," he cried, "and soon all other cities built upon this waterway. The waters will recede, but they will have to rebuild a major portion of those cities."

I was aghast at his comments. "But . . . but . . . the wave . . . .

Where will it end?" I gasped.

"Come," he said once again, grasping me firmly by the arm: "we will follow it."

Soon we were hovering over the top of the wave, its sound terrifying to hear. Ahead lay a large lake, around which was built a great city with many towering skyscrapers. With an ear-splitting roar the wave crashed upon the shore, toppling buildings, swamping the shore-line for many miles, before receding into the lake itself, thus causing a dramatic rise in the water levels. The silence which followed was eerie. All about, cars and the remnants of homes floated in the now still waters; no sound came from what had been a vast and prosperous city. The lake itself appeared to have increased its size by some eight miles all round, leaving little which had not been devastated. I gazed at him, intensely moved, searching his face for an answer.

"Toronto," he said: "but it will rise again, stronger and more positive. It will become a city of Light."

After a moment's pause, while I digested this, he continued: "Come, we must move on. 'Tis time now to move southward." I followed his lead and turned away from the scene of destruction below. Again the mists closed about me, but soon we were hovering over illustrious cities now reduced to chaos, much havoc having been wreaked upon them. Again I gazed at him questioningly.

"California," was his terse comment.

The distress here appeared to be far greater than I had seen so far. Three great cities lay below us and it was as though a giant hand had sliced them away from the mainland, turning them overnight into small offshore islands. Much rescue and salvage work was under way here, the remnants of the population seeking whatever they could find in the midst of the rubble. There was little hope in their eyes, having been constantly battered by the forces of nature, their once-prosperous way of life wiped out in a series of cruel strokes.

As we hovered over this havoc, I could not help but wonder about the many millions who had migrated to this state during the past years. Had they been motivated to do so merely that they might undergo such an experience? I wondered. Here my reverie was interrupted by the Atlantean.

"It is so. Nothing happens by chance — all lies within the law of just repayment. Many are being given the opportunity to face positively just such a situation, having failed to do so during the latter portion of the Atlantean era." He paused, then resumed speaking. "Now we must travel towards the northern lands. Follow me."

Again we entered the mists. Once they cleared, London lay beneath our feet. The scene here shocked me more than any other I had witnessed. The mighty tidal barriers, never fully completed due to the vagaries of human nature, lay twisted on their sides and the destruction caused by flooding was vast. The entire inner area of the city now lay under water. Being a city which was criss-crossed by underground tunnels, the waters had found an ease of entry, and the city had literally drowned overnight. What boats there were lay wrecked at their moorings, and any movement there was took place in the air, for little moved upon the surface.

Thankfully, the mists closed in on me once again and we moved forward to a new point. As the mists cleared again the city of Paris lay beneath us. This once beautiful city now had a new face — it bore a greater resemblance to Venice than to the elegant city I had loved. In many places the Seine had burst its banks, with resulting havoc as its waters had poured into the city. Here, however, many boats were operative and rescue work was under way.

The voice of my teacher cut across the vision. "We must now move forward in the time scale some four and twenty months and return to the Americas. Much that you observe here you must endeavour to record mentally, for you must forewarn the people at a later time." Feeling a familiar sense of dread at these words, we entered a thickening mist and the sensation was accompanied by an intensification of the now well-known buzzing sound.

As the mists began to clear I could see large areas of farmland, where life appeared to be continuing as it had for centuries, unhurried and harmonious. These farmed areas soon gave way to the burnt grasslands where vast herds of cattle grazed. In the far distance was the coast-line and even from this vantage point I could see the great inroads the ocean had made; land which had once sustained Man now lay deep beneath the surface of the ocean.

As we drew closer to the remnants of civilization I noted with interest the behaviour of a group of people who, in the main, appeared to be having great difficulty in adjusting to the recent happenings. They were gathered in the open air, for whatever reason, and were clustered around a portable television set, the voice of the announcer barely audible above the hubbub. The strident tones of one woman, her face grey with worry, pierced the babble.

"Jus' cain't unnerstan' why the President cain't sen' in the National Guard . . . . . ."

"Hold it folks," shouted one man excitedly, turning up the volume on the set, "there's sumpin' comin' over . . . ."

". . . . and it appears to be heading direct towards the earth. From the size of the object, scientists discount the theory that it might be Halley's Comet, said by many to be due to appear about this time, although there is some talk that it might even be a planetoid. Sports news next on 4 XYZ. Stay tuned . . . ."

The set was turned off in disgust and the group fell to discussing this latest threat to their peace of mind.

The scene below kept changing. Although I was apparently maintaining my position in the vicinity, time was passing. Soon my attention was drawn to the sun, its light now partially obscured by an object, which as I watched, daily grew larger. At times I was able to observe the night sky, which was lit by the lurid glow cast by the glowing ball hurtling towards the earth. From its side a huge tail of flame was clearly visible.

I was again taken into the vicinity of the group I had earlier noted, and as before, they were transfixed by the telecast. "Scientists continue to debate the origin of the fire-ball said to be heading towards the earth. Few of them expect it actually to reach us, for, they say, it will be certain to burn up in the atmosphere. Today, a communique issued from the White House asks you all to remain calm and . . . ."

With a loud hoot, bedlam broke out among the spectators. "Calm! Calm they say! — how in the hell do they expect us to be calm? That durned thing could come down right in our back yards!"

"Now then Martha, you always did exaggerate. What makes you think it's gonna hit us, eh? It's a helluva big world.

Besides, they jus' said it wus sure to burn up in the
atmosphere . . . ."

As time passed it soon became apparent that the scientific
prognostications were grossly inaccurate, and frantic efforts
were now being made to ascertain the fire-ball's impact. The
sky by day was darkened by the approaching flaming mass and
the night sky was lit by its lurid glow. The people were
transfixed in terror, none knowing for sure where to head for
safety, so all simply watched the skies in fear, with an anxious
eye cast now and again upon the television, awaiting some
positive instruction. At this point a sudden announcement cut
across the relay of a ball game.

"This afternoon the White House has issued a warning to
the people of the States of Texas and Oklahoma advising all to
prepare for possible impact by the fire-ball, and predict that
these States may well take the full brunt of the collision.
However, they still hope that it will bypass the land and fall
harmlessly into the ocean. We ask you . . . ."

Pandemonium broke loose at this announcement, the
majority of the listeners becoming hysterical, few managing to
achieve anything of a positive nature. All were intent on how
they might save that which they had, with little certain
knowledge of how that might be achieved. Meanwhile the
planetoid drew closer to the earth. Five days later it collided,
the fiery mass tearing into the earth with an enormous roar.
The sound of the collision was deafening in itself, the resultant
destruction too terrible to relate as the land seemed to blow
apart. Very soon this was followed by a series of terrific
explosions which rent apart the land which remained. The
planetoid had landed in the vicinity of an underground silo,
setting off the nuclear deterrent hidden beneath the land and
adding an even greater terror to the burden of the people of
Earth.

"Why? Why is it necessary?" I asked, deeply shaken by that
which I had been forced to observe.

The Atlantean took my arm, seeking to calm my emotions.
"It is the time of cleansing. Some will perish by fire, others by
water, still more through the ravages of war, as the Age begins
to sink into chaos. If Man is wise he will heed these warnings.
Sadly, it is all too rare that wisdom surfaces in time." His tone

was infinitely sad, his face shadowed. "Now it is time for you to return to your daily routine. Cogitate upon that which you have witnessed, for one day you must share it with others."

Here the mists began to close about me again and I lost consciousness.

Chapter 7

Whenever I cast my mind back over the past, one name always emerged out of the mists of time to haunt me: Mneb-Ra. Even now, it still had the power to chill me. With the recent researching into past memories, this name — and its chill overtones — kept surfacing. Back in my mind's eye, as fresh as if it were yesterday, came the vision of that dread time — the time when I had abused the power given to me, along with the trust of the one being whom I respected more than any other. Into my mind's eye came the vision of my mentor, Wen Shu.

"It is time to return once more into your past and I must warn you that much of what you will experience will disturb you. Normally, we would not make such detail available, but it does provide the key to much which has troubled you in recent years. Endeavour to look at the experience dispassionately and realize that all have fallen from the God-like state at some point in time and must thereafter make full reparation. That which I am about to reveal is the lifetime spent as Mneb-Ra, a name you must bear until all within your Group Soul are freed from the pull of matter and progressed to the point of conscious reality.

"Relax — and know that I am with you at all times." Here he bent over me, again placing one hand upon my brow and the other upon the crown of my head. The familiar sensations assailed me, my head swam, my gaze misted over and I slipped from consciousness.

A city lay before me, glistening in the morning sunlight, not unlike some rare mirage. The buildings were constructed of a shimmering white stone which reflected the rays of the sun.

The roofs were a wonder in themselves, being composed of a reddish-gold material, some twisted into elaborate spires, some domed, and others with traceries like cobwebs upon them. There was no sign of rust or decay anywhere and the walls of many of the buildings had impressive embellishments upon them in different coloured hues. Trees and flowering plants of an astonishing range and beauty abounded and many waterfalls were visible. The city appeared to be constructed upon a series of terraces, all of which lent greatly to the over-all beauty of the scene.

I noted many people, and these astounded me more than the city itself. Very tall, wearing little in the way of clothing, their bodies were decorated or tattooed in coloured whorls or stripes. This tended to give them an alien look to my Western eyes, yet there was something very striking about their appearance. There appeared to be two races, the majority being a handsome race with a bluish tinge to their skin and hair of a copper-red colour. This in itself was worn long, but plaited under rather elaborate head-dresses. Created out of gold, these were either helmet-like or fantasy creations, not unlike feathers in their design. Many appeared to have webbed fingers, which, together with the embellishments upon their bodies, made them appear like giant birds of prey.

I came to a halt before a rather impressive building, the frontage of which fell in a series of gentle levels, each overflowing with flowering plants. The sound of cascading water caught my attention and I turned to observe a fountain before which I had stopped. Gazing into the pool I received a tremendous shock. The reflection was that of a man of some forty years of age, immensely tall, with a yellowish-red skin tone! Withdrawing slightly, I stared in amazement at my body which was decorated in blue and gold whorls, and upon which was little more than an elongated white loincloth, held at the waist by a heavy golden belt. Upon my head I felt the heavy weight of a metallic head-dress. Returning to the pool I gazed cautiously at my reflection, which gave back a picture of heavy coarse features and deep-set piercing eyes — quite unlike the majority of the people I had noted. The over-all impression was one of a fearsome Mongolian primitive.

Here my inspection was rudely interrupted by a voice calling loudly. "Mneb-Ra! Mneb-Ra! Whatever ails you? Come, our father awaits us."

Turning in the direction of the voice I noted a girl of the fair race gazing curiously at me. Her beauty was quite astonishing and my heart leaped, as it always did, when my gaze fell upon my half-sister Ilese. Like some pagan goddess, her body was also deeply patterned with blue-gold whorls, a brief gold cloth held at the waist by a wide belt being the only clothing she wore. A sculpted golden head-dress protected her head, from which her deep red hair fell in a long plait. Upon her brow a large amethyst masked her third eye.

She continued to gaze at me curiously. "Why were you staring into the pool? You have not dwelt upon your image in many years."

I ignored her question, unable to provide a sensible answer. "What is it that our father, Imros, wishes of us?" I asked, anxious to divert her questions.

"Matters of State, as you well know," she retorted. "I simply do not understand you today: are you quite well?" she asked, peering closely at me.

"Yes. Yes, of course," I answered rather brusquely, feeling an impatience I rarely felt with her. "Let us proceed into the chamber before they send a messenger in search of us." I grasped her hand and strode quickly into the palatial building before us.

We eventually entered a large hall filled in the main with the members of the bluish-tinged race, although here and there were members of the yellow race and those greeted me warmly as I passed among them. At the back of the hall was a great dais upon which was the ornate chair of office. This was composed almost entirely of gold and studded with precious gems. Upon this seat sat an aged man, who none the less retained his handsome features, being a striking member of the fair race. This was Imros, Priest-King of the Toltecs, now some six hundred and seventy earth years, yet showing no signs of physical weariness or disability, his handsome features still strong, his bearing majestic. As always, when I gazed upon my father, I was filled with deep affection and awe. He was the last of the Apostolic line and the guardian of the sacred wisdom passed to him by the Initiators. These were the great

Cosmic and Planetary beings who had acted as the Teachers for our people since the establishment of life upon our continent. Communication was only possible between the Priest-Kings and the Initiators and this in turn had led to the almost perfect state of affairs which existed upon our planet.

In our society, when the state of Priest-King consciousness was achieved, the Ra appendix was dropped, for this meant 'Child of the Emperor of the Sun.' The prefix 'I' was then assumed, indicating that the Priest-King was now controlled by the Will of the One God, the Source, or the I AM. One day I too hoped to reach that stage of initiation, as had my half-sister Ilese.

Catching sight of us, Imros beckoned us forward, taking his leave of the throng about him. "Come my children, there is much to discuss and you are a little tardy in your arrival," he chided, looking at us both with deep affection: "your brother Mnas-Ra awaits and there are urgent matters of State which we must resolve before this day has ended." Here we left the throng and entered a side chamber which in turn led into a large sunlit patio, within which the central feature of all our homes — the fountain — scattered its cooling energies. Around the pool were clustered many flowering shrubs and plants which filled the air with a heavenly fragrance, the whole area being gently shaded by a large fruit-bearing tree.

Seated by the pool was our sister Laroo-Ra, a full-blooded Toltec and a great beauty. Like all the full blood line, she had hair the colour of beaten copper and a skin like rose petals. Her features were deeply feminine with heavily-lidded eyes which were a great feature of her looks, and on her forehead a small dish-shaped silver medallion masked her third eye. Near the tree stood Queen Khalata, the chief consort of Imros. She was also his sister and had been chosen for the role of Queen in order that the pure Apostolic line might not be defiled. A rather fearsome character, she carried upon her shoulder a huge bird which appeared to be half owl and half eaglet, looking rather like a flat-faced eagle from a distance. She was the only one in our land who could communicate telephathically with the birds and I felt certain that she used this odd creature to spy on those for whom she had no liking.

Pacing back and forth within the patio was our brother,

Mnas-Ra. A tall bronzed figure with the shock of red hair gathered into a large plait common to the Toltec race, he waited impatiently for our arrival. As the eldest son of Imros, he was destined one day to become Priest-King and therefore had an air of authority and some arrogance about him.

"At last — I was beginning to wonder if anyone would ever appear. I have many . . . ."

"Patience my son," interrupted our father, holding up his hand for silence. "Let us sit and relax amidst the blossoms; it will aid our discussions."

I was somewhat irritated by my brother's manner. "I agree. The day is warm and I am a little weary."

Sinking to the floor around the pool, we watched as Imros produced a sheaf of State documents.

"As you are all aware, we are being harassed on our northern borders by the wild men of those far distant lands of the snows. The Semites will simply not remain within their allotted borders and make continual raids upon our peoples, causing much destruction and carrying off many of our women into bondage. They demand larger tracts of land, despite the fact that much that they currently inhabit was unlawfully taken. The Turanians, whose lands border theirs are not prepared to intervene on our behalf, even though they could so easily contain that border for us. We must therefore find some method of bringing them within our fold."

I interrupted angrily at this point. "Let us attack and teach them a well-deserved lesson. Those upstarts . . . ."

"Oh, Mneb-Ra!" my brother cried wearily, "all that you ever consider is force. Our peoples have fought for centuries and it has resolved nothing. We must find another solution."

"I agree," my father interposed peacefully: "our peoples cannot war forever, although I understand your fiery nature, my son," he said, patting my knee. "The blood of your people rises within you and you understand not our talk of peace."

At this point, Ilese, who had quietly observed the discussions without comment, intervened. "What else are we to do? If the Turanians refuse to assist, how can we bring this situation under control?" She had misgivings as to why she and Laroo-Ra had been drawn into this matter of State, and was experiencing some difficulty in quelling thoughts which were entering into her mind. She herself was a Seeress, serving largely within the High Temple, and she did not much care for the direction the conversation was taking.

Imros gazed at her with deep affection, his face tinged with sadness. "It is necessary for us to make a blood pact with the Turanians. In this way we shall draw the kingdoms together, aid the evolution of your brother's people and contain our northern borders."

There was a deathly silence at these words, for both Mnas-Ra and I were fiercely devoted to our sister and could not believe our ears. Taking her hand in his, Imros continued quietly. "Of course, it must be with your consent, my daughter. As the eldest daughter of the line and a full Initiate, you are well fitted to this role the State asks of you."

Her face ashen, Ilese cast her eyes about wildly, looking for some escape from this fate, although her training had long prepared her for the possibility of such an occurrence. Mnas-Ra appeared to have been turned to stone. He had long harboured the desire to take her as his wife one day and he remained mute in the face of our father's request. Imros spoke quietly, breaking the gloom which had suddenly fallen upon the sunlit scene. "A young Turanian prince holds the land adjacent to our northern borders and he seeks a wife. The melding of the races can, I believe, be achieved, by the joining of the Blood Royal." He spoke with great gentleness, pathos and love, holding Ilese compassionately to him.

The fire on my tongue was suddenly stilled, for Imros had himself followed this course of action long ago and had chosen a wife from the rising Turanian tribes. With this act he had endeavoured to expand the consciousness of the rising race and I was the product of that liason. I stole a look at Queen Khalata, whose grim features indicated that she was not agreeable to this action at all. I knew that it was vital for my people to establish themselves and to seek occult awareness, but I had never ever considered that my beloved sister might become a pawn in that progress. According to her expression, neither had Queen Khalata.

Ilese continued to sit quietly, her eyes downcast, the sorrow she felt evident from her posture. Imros continued gently, "I would not of course force any child of mine into a liason which was abhorrent to her, but I would beg you to consider my request, my child. It goes beyond personal feelings and affairs of State. I do not have to illustrate to you just what is at stake here."

She slowly lifted her head, her eyes filled with deep sorrow and resignation, her face set in a determined expression. "I will do as you wish Father. I was simply caught unawares. Please excuse me." She left the courtyard with slow footsteps and walked towards her quarters, Laroo-Ra getting up swiftly to follow her. Unable to contain my feelings any longer, I excused myself and rushed blindly from the courtyard.

Some months later Ilese was duly married amidst the pomp and ceremony our people had come to accept as normal from the Royal House. During the festivities I had the opportunity to mix with my kinsmen, linked now through the marriage alliance. The bridegroom was little more than a strutting braggart who drew no respect from me. I could scarcely believe that Imros could have chosen such an ill-match for my beloved sister and deeply resented the whole situation. There was much I still had to learn about the control of my fiery nature and this Imros understood well. He had been aware of the depth of my feelings for Ilese, also that Mnas-Ra desired her for his bride. To prevent bloodshed at a later date and to ensure co-operation between the races he had brought about the liason. He could not have foreseen the conflict that lay ahead. If he had, he would not have acted in the manner he did or have taken any of the actions which preceded them.

Chapter 8

Some two years later Imros called Mnas-Ra and me into his private quarters and as I entered his features were grave and I sensed an atmosphere of suppressed tension. I stiffened, drawing myself up to my full height, towering over my brother. I sensed conflict and was more than ready to face it. Imros, aware of my reaction, placed his arm around my waist and drew my brother and I together. "Come, let us sit, this is no time for hostility. What I have to say must remain completely confidential, to be shared with no other outside this room."

Mnas-Ra shot me a look which was both curious and hostile. He also was aware of the undercurrent and was wary.

Imros looked from one to the other of us, his face filled with love. "It is almost time my sons, for me to relinquish this cloak of matter, time for me to return to the peace of the Realms of Light. I am wearied by the continual arguments in the Council of the Elders and I feel that I cannot hold this form for much longer."

I stared at Mnas-Ra, whose face was suddenly suffused with great joy. Although he loved Imros deeply, he was impatient to begin his chosen task as Priest-King.

Taking his hand, Imros continued: "However, I have pondered long and reached a difficult decision, one which I trust you will both respect. As you are both aware, the time of the Toltec people fades and the hour of the Turanian race is nigh. With that in mind, long ago did I choose a wife from the midst of the Turanian people and my well-loved son Mneb-Ra was the fruit of that liason. It is my desire that the races meld, that they learn to live in peace with each other. The Turanians need much guidance, they know not our occult ways and practices and we must instruct them that they in turn may carry on the tasks we have begun. They require at their head one who understands their needs, and one of their own kind."

At this Mnas-Ra leaped to his feet. "What are you suggesting, O Imros? I have long been trained for this role. I understand well the requirements of the new race; have I not contended with my brother these many years and sought to curb his warlike ways?"

"Yes, yes," said Imros placatingly, "and it is not my intention to rob you of the power that I know you will wield so well. After much inner conflict I have, however, decided that it is time to break the long-standing tradition of our people in an effort to resolve the difficulty.

"It is my decision that you will become King, Mnas-Ra, for you are strong, yet possess a cool head. You will maintain the peace in our land, guiding the people in the manner I have striven to do. A strong King retains peace in the land."

Mnas-Ra rose, flushed with anger. "Our people have always been ruled by Priest-Kings. Am I not therefore qualified, have I not undertaken all of the necessary initiations? The Crown and the Key belong to me alone."

Imros rose and faced him, his frame now visibly ageing, yet retaining sufficient strength to appear to dwarf his elder son.

"The decision is mine alone, my son." His voice was firm, yet filled with a gentle sadness. "I have not reached this decision lightly. For many years have I pondered, having the interest of both races at heart. It grieves me that I cannot stay to bring about the melding of the races, but I grow weary and must leave in the hands of those I trust the task which will test the abilities of all. To that end I have decided that Mneb-Ra must become High Priest and rule alongside you. The Key will be his symbol of authority in the land."

I sat astonished, my heart filled with joy, a joy I had never before known. Never in my wildest dreams had I ever imagined a situation such as this. As I observed the by-play between Imros and Mnas-Ra, a thought struck me and impelled me to intervene.

"Why not make me King and Mnas-Ra High Priest?" I shouted eagerly. "He is more fitted than I to the ways of the Priesthood, whilst I long to resolve the matters on our borders."

Imros gazed at me with sadness in his eyes. "It is for that reason that I have reached this decision. You, my son, need to learn the inner way and to temper your impatience with wisdom. In turn, you must teach your people how they might also find inner strength. As you rightly say, Mnas-Ra is better fitted for that role, yet because of that he will make a finer King. You must learn to still your fiery temperament within spiritual discipline."

Mnas-Ra sat in shocked silence, his world in pieces about him. The look he shot me was filled with deep hatred for having taken half of his birthright from him. Noting this, Imros said quietly, "Little will be achieved if those whom I have chosen descend to personal enmity. Did your sister Ilese not take the bitter cup when the needs of the nation were great? Are you both any less than her?"

We were both stung into resentful silence by this remark.

Rising slowly, Imros extended his hands to us and bade us join our hands in unity. "Come, let us meditate upon the happenings of the day within the temple," he said, and led us unhurriedly from his chambers.

Some weeks following his revelation, Imros called us once more into his inner chamber. "Well my sons, you have both had ample time to dwell upon my decisions. What are your reactions, in the light of your meditations?"

Mnas-Ra and I gazed at each other before answering, Mnas-Ra stepped forward and knelt before Imros. "My heart is heavy, for I feel that I am judged inadequate. However, I will accept your will in this matter, for I know that you are ever guided by the Initiators."

His face filled with deep love and compassion, Imros urged him to his feet. "You have decided well my son. The people will have a fine King in you." Turning to me he asked, "And you, Mneb-Ra, what is your decision?"

Looking deep into his eyes I replied haltingly: "If it . . . be your wish . . . Father . . . I will accept this role." Dropping to my knees, I kissed his hand.

His face alight with joy he embraced us both, leading us to his small private courtyard. "My sons, you both make me very happy. My decision was correct, the people shall have two positive rulers and together you will bring about the melding of the races." Seating ourselves around the small fountain we awaited his further instruction. "There is much for you both to become acquainted with before you accept your roles of State. Some time soon we must all journey to Zoltun, where I will instruct you both on that which lies there."

"Zoltun?" we both echoed, mystified.

"The Forbidden One?" continued Mnas-Ra. "What can we possibly learn there?"

Imros gave us a grave look before replying. "It is the true power in the land. Hidden deep within its depths lies the gift — if one may call it that — of the Transients."

We both gazed at him transfixed, for this was strange news to us both. I regained my senses first. "Do you mean the space wanderers Father? I thought they were but a myth, something a boy interests himself with."

D

Mnas-Ra interposed swiftly: "What gift is this you speak of? Why do you say it is the true power in the land?"

Imros answered us both. "Knowledge of the gift of the Transients has been passed from Priest-King to Priest-King, within whom lies the responsibility to ensure that the power hidden within Zoltun does not fall into the wrong hands. It will become your task, Mnas-Ra, to ensure that the Solar Particle remains hidden deep within the forbidden mountain. Should knowledge of its existence ever become common knowledge many would seek to obtain it for themselves and great destruction would then take place within our fair land."

"But what is it?" asked Mnas-Ra impatiently.

Imros rose slowly to his feet and began to pace the courtyard. "The Solar Particle was brought to this planet by the Transients in the early days. They themselves are said to have come from the Sun, although we cannot be too certain of that. It seems more than likely that they were not of our Solar system and were possibly of a different aspect of the evolutionary scale. They were certainly non-humans and were deeply curious as to human development. Their interest in us was clinical and detached. They sought in the main to oversee our progress and apparently did endeavour to share some of their knowledge, but there were few who could absorb it fully. Such interference in the development of Man does not assist his growth in the long term; in fact, it tends to retard growth. They left behind the Solar Particle, which is of such immense strength that for safety it is encased within a leaden cauldron and buried deep beneath Zoltun. To keep away the curious, the priesthood created the stories you know so well about the Forbidden One, in an effort to ensure that the Particle remains hidden."

We sat in stunned silence, for the revelations were difficult to comprehend. "When must we journey there?" asked Mnas-Ra.

"Soon my son, soon," replied Imros, "for my time is drawing nigh. First I have many affairs of State which I must deal with. Let us say, in twenty days from now. Remember, my sons, this knowledge is not to be shared with any other, for the safety of the land depends upon it. Do not mention our intended journey to anyone."

It was with a feeling of elation that we set out some weeks later upon the journey to the Forbidden One. Ahead of us lay a mysterious power, of which no others were aware and the sense of anticipation which affected my brother and me, drew us together and did much to erase the bitterness which had arisen between us of late. It took some three hours to journey by airship to Zoltun. Our mode of travel was silent, the ship hovering above the level of the terrain, projected through space with the aid of a large crystal which we used to tap into the hidden powers within the planet. These forces energized the crystal and gave the airship its motivation. In our land crystals were used for many purposes. As there was no light available once the Sun descended over the horizon (there was no moon at that point in time) the people carried small crystals in the palms of their hands. The light emitted by these was more than sufficient to light one's path. They had many other uses, too. In the main they were used in the Healing Temples, although mostly to heal fractures or broken limbs after accidents. We also used them as a power source in mining, to produce heat or light in our homes, and making rain in the dry seasons.

Below us a grim edifice emerged from the swirling mists. Zoltun — a silent brooding giant — lay below us. Many centuries ago our people had mined the metals which lay deep within this mountain, but now it lay still, chill and forbidden.

Descending from the airship, we began the short walk towards the base of the mountain. As we approached, two elderly priests appeared, apparently expecting our arrival. This I found astonishing, for I personally had no knowledge of these priests, whose garb was strange to me and who appeared even to outdistance Imros in years. Imros greeted them warmly, as if meeting old and valued friends and they ushered us into a small temple hidden in the side of a great tunnel at the base of the mountain.

There was little of note within the temple itself, for it was stark, yet great light filled every portion of it. Obviously an immense crystal was secreted within it to provide such light, but how they came by it I had no idea. The priests now motioned us towards a small chamber and indicated that we should change our attire for that which was hanging within.

The robes were strange, made of a harsh reflective material not unlike metal. The outfit was completed by a rather odd head-dress which completely encased the head, providing only small slits for seeing and breathing. Feeling decidedly ill at ease we set off into the tunnels, riding upon a small carriage which hung from a central rod suspended from the roof of the cavern.

The journey in itself seemed endless, the atmosphere was dank and chill and I was thankful for the protection afforded by the strange attire. Eventually we arrived in a large cavern and stepped from the carriage. Ahead lay a deep hole cut into the floor of the cavern, this being topped with a large rock cut like some gigantic plug. The atmosphere here was different and I was aware of pulsating vibrations, the like of which I had never encountered.

Imros indicated that we should stand well back from the rock plug. His voice when he spoke was strangely muffled by the protective head-gear.

"This, my sons, is the Solar Particle. In itself it provides a force which could well destroy the entire planet. In the wrong hands, a great destructive force would be set loose in the universe. That must never be allowed to happen. Hidden here, it assists in preventing unwelcome planetary visitors penetrating our atmosphere and this is its major function today. He who has the Particle has power in the land. Know that you are now its guardians. Protect it well, reveal its presence to no other than those to whom you in turn will hand the Seal of Office." He turned aside and indicated that it was time for us to return.

A week later, a further summons drew us to the chambers of Imros and here we sat patiently awaiting further instruction that our new office fitted us to receive. Imros spoke: "Having revealed the position of the Solar Particle, it is now time that you both became acquainted with the source of spiritual power in our land. Let us now journey to the High Temple and I will reveal to you the Alnetic Key." Following a short distance behind him, as protocol demanded, we climbed to the glistening structure which stood on high, apart from all other structures in the land. There were twelve small outer temples gathered around the large inner temple, all of which were constructed of the glistening white stone so common to our land. Within the large inner temple the High Priest trained the acolytes and ministered to the spiritual needs of the people.

I myself had spent many years within the temple undergoing the training and initiations necessary for my office. Like Mnas-Ra, I had also reached the level of Master Initiate and the High Temple was the place I sought whenever I required peace and respite from the pressure of Court life. In all of these years I had never set eyes on the Great Key, hidden deep within an inner chamber of the temple. This chamber was entered by none but Imros.

As he unlocked this inner chamber, we stepped within, filled with a deep curiosity, yet also with a grave sense of foreboding. Unlike the chamber wherein was hidden the Solar Particle, this chamber was filled with light and the pulsating energy of love. Stepping forward, Imros pulled aside a heavy curtain behind which, upon a dais, stood the Key. I gazed at it searchingly. At present it was silent, yet its surface glowed and reflected a deep violet light. It was really a gigantic prism encased within an oval casing made apparently of gold. As I continued to gaze within it, there swirled beneath its surface all the colours then known to men and angels.

Imros stepped forward and bade us do likewise. "The case of the Key is not fashioned from gold," he smiled at me, aware of my thoughts on the Key, "for gold would not be sufficiently strong enough to withstand its power. The case is blended from all of the metals native to our land and is extremely strong. Harder than rock, yet more malleable. Now I wish you to sit and observe." Seating himself before the Key he sank into deep meditation.

After some ten minutes he raised his head and removed the amethyst jewel which masked his third eye; he then commenced to focus a power through his third eye into the Key and as he did so, it became active and sprang to life. It soon became mirror-like and the colours of the spectrum began to flash from its depths. We became aware of intense energies projecting from the Key and soon we became swept up in these, becoming temporarily part of the Key itself. The colours swirled all about us and as we entered into its energy field, visions appeared all about us. I was thrust into a great conflict, surrounded on all sides by members of the Turanian race. Attacking on all fronts were Toltecs, the fury of their attack arousing within myself such great anger that I had immense difficulty in holding myself in restraint. Pillage and looting were rampant, largely by my own people who were apparently seeking to satisfy a strange blood-lust.

"Why . . .? Why . . .?" I came back to consciousness slowly, deeply disturbed by the vision. I gazed at Imros beseechingly, unable to speak, yet seeking an answer to what I had experienced.

He answered my unspoken question. "That, my son, is the reason I have taken my decision. You and your brother must seek to prevent such bloodshed. What you both visioned within the Key is what could well come about if power is misused. You must both ensure that it does not. It is a warning."

Linking arms, he led us towards the Key itself. "Touch it not, for it dissolves matter on impact," he warned. We hurriedly withdrew. From a safe distance we studied it: from here it resembled a pulsating colour-changing bubble.

"The primary use of the Key is to enable those empowered so to do, to communicate with the Hierarchy, the Initiators. Its power is spiritual. It must never fall into the hands of those who would use it for political ends, for that would pervert its power. The result would be the crumbling of our civilization, as you so recently envisioned. The Key is in fact, a force-field of compacted energy molecules attuned to the psychic or creative portion of the race-group brain centres. Great care must be taken to ensure that it is never abused, for it would result in great mental stress for the races."

Here he bade us withdraw from the inner chamber whilst he concentrated for a while upon the Key, leaving us to mull over that which we had experienced. After a short period he rejoined us and led us back to his inner chambers in the palace, where we continued our joint discussions long into the night.

Chapter 9

During the two years which followed, Mnas-Ra and I spent much of our time with Imros, absorbing all that was necessary to fit us for our future roles. It was during this period that we came together again, although the closeness of our youth had gone for ever. Understanding now a little of what lay ahead of us and gaining a little insight into the great difficulties which had forced Imros into his decision, we attempted to put aside our differences and learn our Statecraft. During this period Ilese sent many pleas for help, for she was greatly abused physically by her husband. Unused to such treatment, she begged for assistance and release. Imros however, would not hear of aid being despatched to her. He stated that she had within the self talents which would assist her to resolve her problems and that she must endeavour to deal with the task unaided. We felt at first that he was being unnecessarily harsh, but he brought about a realization within us that to aid her as she requested would nullify the act of bringing the peoples together, so with heavy hearts we had to leave Ilese to her fate.

Finally came the day when Imros called all his family together, even summoning Ilese from her northern home. The palace was filled with a bustle and an air of suppressed excitement. None realized the full portent of the day, for none knew of the agreement between Imros and his sons. Queen Khalata dominated the scene, quelling the excitement of the younger members of the family with a powerful glare, the ever-present bird upon her shoulder lending an air of fear to the scene. Between the Queen and myself there was no love lost. She had always resented the taking of a new wife by Imros and had made certain that none of her offspring was overlooked in the palace hierarchy. I had often felt that she involved herself with forces which could bring destruction to the land, yet could never openly say so. I merely observed and took great care in her presence.

Standing by the side of my gentle mother, Tibith, a princess in her own right, I drew her close to me in a protective manner. She was deeply devoted to Imros, although never allowed too close a contact by Queen Khalata, and I knew that the news of his departure would be a great shock to her.

Silence descended as Imros entered the room. His features were grave and his eyes filled with such sadness that even the Queen was stilled. She sensed change in the air and was ever alert to the need to remain at the forefront.

Seating himself, Imros bade us all draw close. "I have sad news for you all, yet I know that you in turn will rejoice with me. It is time to terminate my stay upon the planet and I have called you all together to take my leave of you." At these words great wails arose from the female members of the family except for Queen Khalata who, with eyes gleaming and mouth pursed, drew herself up to her full height. She sensed power and was ready to take it.

When the tears had subsided, Imros dropped his bombshell. "In leaving, I have taken a deeper decision than any before me. My beloved son Mnas-Ra will, as befits him, become King — and my equally beloved son Mneb-Ra shall become High Priest."

The Queen leaped to her feet with a curse on her lips. "You shall not rob my son of his birthright, Imros. I . . . ." She was silenced by the look Imros gave her as he turned to her: it was clear, steady and inflexible. She lowered her gaze and sank reluctantly to her seat.

"The decision is mine, and mine alone, and my sons have agreed to accept this decision. Any who would seek to set apart that which is decreed will bring down the kingdom itself." He paused, looking at her penetratingly, before he continued: "I am quite certain you would not wish that to happen, my dear wife." Shaking her head, unable to return his gaze, she remained silent.

My mother grasped my arm, her eyes shining. Her face radiant, she turned to Imros and was about to speak when he shook his head, indicating that no comment was necessary. His eyes were filled with deep affection for her and I was greatly moved. Ilese held my gaze across the room, her eyes filled with tears, her features sharpened by the years of unhappiness. Her thoughts blended with mine, for she too was joyful at my sudden unexpected elevation, but could not find words to express it without hurting Mnas-Ra.

One by one the family took its sad leave-taking of Imros. Although all were aware that death existed not, it was the loss of this strong and well-loved figure from their daily lives that grieved them so. Finally, Mnas-Ra and I were left alone within the chamber to receive the relative symbols of office and take our final farewells.

With the crowning of Mnas-Ra as King and my installation as High Priest, life assumed a more intense purpose. For my part, I was determined to play my part to the full, seeking to aid my people to reach a higher state of consciousness. Mnas-Ra for his part immersed himself in his Kingly role, determined to ensure that peace would remain a vital part in the life of the people. As we sought to fulfil the dream of Imros, a harmony arose between us in the years which followed.

All was not well within the confines of the palace however. Queen Khalata, now elevated to a position of almost total power — with Mnas-Ra unable or unwilling to restrict her — sought to bring about my downfall and that of all around her who had fallen foul of her during the reign of Imros. She was now openly consorting with darker forces, creating a huge pit within the palace grounds wherein she kept great flesh-eating birds with talons which could tear a man apart. Ostensibly, she kept these for riding, for they were so immense that they could not fly, but many in our land used them to ride upon as they could cover the ground at an amazing rate. Some of those she trained were over twenty feet high. Having the ability to communicate telepathically with her foul pets, Queen Khalata set a trap for my gentle mother which resulted in her being torn apart in the bird pit.

In spite of my tremendous anger and his own horror, Mnas-Ra refused to intervene, stating that his mother had the right to her pets despite this most unfortunate accident. Realizing that I would achieve nothing through him, I began to keep a watchful eye upon Queen Khalata through the Key, which at least brought me protection. Largely due to the freedom now granted to the Queen, forces which had long lain dormant within our peoples began to surface and many were drawn into the practice of dark rites; stories of the sacrifice of animals within these rites were soon rife. Sadly, many of my own race became caught up in the satanic practices and this brought an intensification of my work in the temple. So many of my own people had little understanding of the power of thought and with the releasing and use of the latent dark forces, great and ugly thought-forms began to make themselves evident on the planet. Taking hideous shapes, often like some gigantic fire-breathing serpent, they terrified the populace. Still being fairly psychic, they could observe the end product of the destructive thought patterns, but lacked the understanding of how to deal with them. I intensified my effort to instruct the people on the correct use of thought, but to little avail.

Among the Toltecs, differing problems emerged. In the past, the men had been content to become warriors, relegating the women to the task of temple servers. In these tasks they had learned to develop their mental powers and extend their intuitive abilities. Throughout many centuries this had led to a situation wherein the women became the true rulers because of their spiritual self-control. With a settled land and less need for warriors, men became restless, eager to acquire the same powers as the womenfolk. This further increased the pressures upon me in my role as High Priest.

With the passing of the years, the ugly thought-forms unleashed by Man increased. I spent myself in long laborious hours of instruction, yet despite this, the forces did not abate. The people grew restless and increasing demands were made upon the King to conquer this new terror which was rising against them. The people felt that a new enemy had arisen and they greatly feared it, for it did not respond to physical force. In a sense they were correct in their assumption, yet failed to understand that they were the creators of it. The continual pressure eventually drew Mnas-Ra to the temple where he begged me to release the Key to him in order that he might destroy the thought patterns. His only desire was the defence of the people, having their well-being in mind. I could not accede to his request and brought his attention to the instruction of Imros — that it must never be used for any other purpose than spiritual direction. I also realized that if I gave in, for I too was hard pressed, the force would, in effect, be turned upon my own people, whose leader I was meant to be. The Turanian blood was rising from deep within me and I refused to turn the force against my own kind.

Shortly after this, a further plea for assistance came from Ilese, who could no longer withstand the cruelties inflicted upon her by her Turanian husband. Fresh from his conflict with me, Mnas-Ra determined to teach the upstart Turanian braggart a lesson he would never forget and set off for the north with a strong force of troopers. Forgetting for once the need to retain a cool head, Mnas-Ra became involved in a short but heated battle with the guards of the Turanian and in an endeavour to avenge Ilese for all the harm done to her in past years, he slew the princeling, thus setting the seal on the tide of events which would soon sweep over our fair land.

On his return, elated with the success of his battle, he again came to the temple and this time demanded that the Key be surrendered to him. Again I repulsed him, realizing that it was but a matter of time before he appeared with an armoured troop to deal with yet another Turanian princeling. Turning to Ilese, we found a way to dismantle the Key without harm to ourselves by using her deep occult knowledge. Choosing the time of night to flee when none would expect to see me, we fled by means of the many underground passages which honeycombed the ground beneath the palace and the city. These led to the coastlands and were used to transport goods, the streets of the city being for the use of pedestrians only. On reaching the coast we set sail for one of the many islands which abounded in the coastal waters, taking care to select one upon which the Turanians had chosen to settle.

Within days, the Key revealed that Mnas-Ra had discovered our flight and was on the way to the coast in search of us with a strong armed guard at his command. Realizing that it would be but a matter of time before he located our refuge, I endeavoured to find some means of disguising our hiding place. In a moment of sheer desperation, I used the Key to call down the ugly thought-forms in the ether and commanded them to mask the site of the island. In so doing, I unwittingly set in motion an unconscious alliance with the Ahriamanic forces, an alliance I would never be able to break during that lifetime.

As time passed I found that not only could I control the thought-patterns at will, but men too. All too soon the ideals of spiritual leadership handed down by Imros were distorted into a tyranny of power lust and total domination of the continent by the Turanians, with myself as their King and High Priest. Soon, the destruction, controlled by the dark forces, spread upon the land. Once fair temples were sacked, my largely illiterate people who did not realize the power which lay in the sacred objects they discovered, broke them apart for their intrinsic value. Retaining the knowledge gained through my Toltec heritage, I utilized the force within the Key to further my now insatiable ambition, little realizing that in this I was little more than a pawn in the Ahriamanic plan for world domination.

I gradually diverted the power of the Key from spiritual usage to that of scientific and political ends and determined that I would wrest from Mnas-Ra, now my bitterest enemy, his final vestige of power — the Solar Particle. With that in my possession, I would rule the earth. Gathering together a large force of men, equipped in the main with laser weapons, we set out on the long journey to the Forbidden One — Zoltun.

However, our progress had been noted by Queen Khalata, who forewarned Mnas-Ra of our intentions and upon our arrival we found a strong force of the King's militia firmly established within the caverns of the Sacred Mountain. An all-out battle commenced, with the fearsome effects of the lasers taking a huge toll on both sides. Deciding that we might only achieve success through entering the caverns from above, I ordered the lasers to be concentrated upon the upper portion of the mountain, with terrifying results. Instead of clearing a path into the mountain itself, it demolished the upper portion, which collapsed upon the hidden caverns, burying Mnas-Ra, his troops and the Solar Particle for ever.

Thwarted in my determination to achieve control of the Solar Particle, I had eliminated my brother only to take on a greater adversary — Queen Khalata. With all her conscious communication with the darker forces she took control in the Toltec-held lands, and so began a conflict which continued for some six centuries. The Toltecs, always the greater number in skill and battle, often reduced my forces to naught, yet with the aid of the Key I rallied and threw fresh forces into the conflict.

The constant battles led to a great deal of migration among

my own people, who sought to find a place wherein they might live in peace. Following several centuries of war and depletion through migration, I set in motion a law which eventually led to the downfall of the Turanian race. Needing desperately to increase our population I passed a law which freed the people from the need to support their children. From that point on they became wards of the State, which would care for them. In the short term it had its desired effect, as the birthrate began to soar, but sadly, it also led to the collapse of family ties and eventually to a decline in the state of marriage. Without family ties chaos ensued, and I, who had led my people to a peak of achievement in savagery, led them eventually to a state of self-destruction.

As the vision began to fade, I returned to consciousness with a very deep sense of regret and anguish at the futility of it all, also an overwhelming feeling of failure. If this is what I did when given spiritual power, how could anyone ever trust me in that field again?

As I sadly pondered on this, I was aware of Imros building up before me. He gazed at me for a moment, then spoke with great gentleness, pathos and love. "My beloved son, I have heaviness of heart, even after all these centuries, for I perpetrated a great injustice upon the karma of all three of you — Mnas-Ra, Ilese and yourself — by making my transition before settling the rising tides of confusion within the land. Hopefully, I deluded myself that the melding of the races would be achieved by the joining of the Blood Royal. I was weary, tired of argument, refusing to listen to the counsel of the Spiritual Elders. The Particle and the Key should have been buried and their hiding places forgotten. We needed no mechanical aids to our progression, but once they were there, we used them — to bring about our own destruction. The Lords of Light were our protection. They warned me of the dangerous road we trod, but I ignored their instructions. With hindsight I accept that I placed too great a burden upon your shoulders and wish to acknowledge the major portion of the blame.

"I bequeath to you my child, your birthright and legacy of the continual presence and guardianship of the Great Ones. You have been trained as a pure channel for this especial time, putting aside the personal and physical self and using only that part of consciousness which is dormant in most human beings. This is my promise. The Great Ones will not fail you. Later in this lifetime you will meet again with Mnas-Ra, this time in the female form. Help him, for together you have much to accomplish." With this, he smiled and faded from my view.

Chapter 10

During my sleep state journeys I became aware of a change in the pattern and rhythm of the discussions with Wen Shu and the Teachers. It appeared to me that I was spending more and more time in the Halls of Learning and less and less time down in the receiving stations or in the lower thought worlds. I sensed that the change was leading towards a cross roads, but if Wen Shu was aware of my curiosity, he made no comment.

One evening he met me as I entered the sleep state, welcoming as ever, his warm smile and open arms an assurance of the affection he had for me. "Come my son, it is time for you to meet with the souls who will one day work alongside you."

I gazed at him humorously: "In this life, or the next?" I said, for I had by now become accustomed to meeting those who were linked with my past.

"In both," he replied, his eyes twinkling. "To achieve this, we must journey to a higher plane than that which we are accustomed to visiting. You may well find some difficulty in adjusting to the light and the intense vibration you will encounter there, so our first visit will be short." Clasping my hand in his he led me towards a small temple, within which we both settled into a meditative silence. After a while he grasped my hand tightly and bade me relax and journey with him.

I was soon aware of an intense light, the brilliance of which made it difficult to focus my gaze. Pervading the atmosphere was a great feeling of love. As I grew used to the radiance I saw that we were standing in a garden of great beauty, the blossoms having a vibrancy and shade I had never encountered before; the very air seemed to be alive. As I gazed about me I noted that the inhabitants of this plane were also vastly different from any I had met before. They appeared to radiate life from every portion of their being and as I met their gaze, I was aware of a deep love flowing towards me.

"I can see what you mean," I whispered to Wen Shu. "Here one could easily feel one had entered into the heavenly spheres and simply avoid all further conscious effort towards growth."

He smiled as he led me forward. "Where are we exactly?" I asked, my curiosity unable to contain itself any longer.

"We are upon one of the higher sub-planes of the fifth or mental plane," he replied. "All those whom you perceive here are to form part of the future race-consciousness that will one day inhabit the Earth-plane. They will become the sixth sub-race of Man, the last race which will be physical and they have been prepared for a very long time for this opportunity. Through them the race of Man will be taken to a more positive level of expression."

"When you say 'the last race which will be physical', just what do you mean?" I asked, rather puzzled by this comment.

"Following the expression of the sixth sub-race, the appearance upon the planet Earth will be undertaken in the etheric form, for Man will by that time have thrown off the pull of matter and incarnate only to aid the progression of the planet itself," he explained.

"Completely?" I questioned somewhat doubtingly, from my awareness of the human race.

"That is what is intended, although there will ever be stragglers who will have to endeavour to catch up before it is too late," he said.

"What happens to those who do not?" I queried.

"Those who, by the end of the Jupiter Period, have not managed to transmute their physical forms into light bodies, will have great difficulty in existing during the final Age of Vulcan. At the end of that period, the planet will have become a plane of light and its purpose as a schoolroom for Man will have ceased." Wen Shu waited to see what effect this would have on me.

"And how far away is that?" I probed eagerly.

He smiled delightedly at me. "Some two billion of your earth years, so I doubt that you need worry yet, my son!"

I grinned rather sheepishly, then recovering, and now anxious to know if it would be during my current sojourn, asked: "When will the new race appear on Earth?"

"They will begin to appear in small numbers during the last quarter of your current century and then in increasing numbers once the Age of Enlightenment has dawned," he replied.

I had by this time received a considerable amount of instruction from the Teachers on this subject and was aware that he spoke of the Golden Age of Aquarius, due to commence officially during the early part of the twenty-first century.

"They all appear so different, almost unreal," I said, turning my gaze back to the inhabitants of this almost dreamlike plane. "Never have I encountered beings such as these before. Will all the new Age peoples be like this?"

Sadly he shook his head. "No my son, these you see here will be the teachers of Man. They will appear among the residue of the races and their task will be to lead the remnants of Mankind toward a fourth dimensional awareness. This can only be achieved if Man will accept the need for brotherhood and universal love, shared without condition."

I gave this some thought, "The fourth dimension is what I term the spirit world, whilst the Earth-plane tends to be three dimensional. How will they achieve their goal? You have said that physical forms will last for some time — how can this come about without the destruction of physical forms?"

He beamed at me, realizing I was grappling with a Cosmic Truth. "No, no, not at all. Physical forms will still have a great part to play in human expression for some time to come, but the race of Man must endeavour to change his outlook. Once again he must embrace his spiritual reality and work towards harmony and Christ-consciousness within himself. At present, Man is constantly at war with himself, refusing, in the main, to acknowledge his Divine origin."

"But just how is Man going to be able to transform into a fourth dimensional being whilst he continues to exist within a three dimensional world?" I cried, still unable to grasp his meaning.

"It will be no easy task, my son," he said gently,

understanding my confusion. "Many forces of Cosmic origin will be brought into play to ensure that this change of consciousness does take place."

"What forces do you speak of?" I asked, half afraid of his answer.

"Some that you cannot understand, my son, but these forces will combine with planetary energies which will be directed to the planet. This is now necessary, for Man has sunk to a level where materialism is the greatest threat to the continued existence of the race of Man. This situation has been brought about largely by the Ahriamanic forces, of course."

"The Ahriamanic forces? Were they not responsible for the downfall of Atlantis?" I queried.

He made a wry face. "Indeed, my son, they certainly assisted in the destruction and extinction of that once fair continent. You must bear in mind, however, that Mankind has free will — he need not heed them or their call."

"Why are they allowed to bring down civilizations?" I cried heatedly.

"Now you begin to talk like a three dimensional being!" he gently remonstrated, his eyes a-twinkle with humour. Realizing too late that he was indeed correct, I stilled my impetuous tongue.

"However," he continued, placing his arm around my shoulders in a gesture of affection, "our purpose in visiting this level is to introduce you to those who have a part to play within your future. You will return here frequently once you have acclimatized to the vibrations here, for there is a great deal that you must learn." With this he led me towards a small group who appeared to be quietly awaiting our arrival.

From this time on, whatever memories I brought forward into the conscious waking state were always of this plane of light, wherein I met, conversed and studied with, many of the souls I had noted during my first visit. Some among them were souls I had known before as Initiate priests in Atlantis; some others were my brother acolytes with whom I had trained in Egypt. With all, I felt a flow of brotherly love which was quite impossible to resist. If the new Age was to lead to such expression on Earth, I could scarce await its commencement.

E

Chapter 11

For weeks I pounded away at my typewriter, almost becoming a recluse in the endeavour to set down the memories, so great was the flood. Opening the gates to that which I had repressed for so many years had unlocked such a depth of awareness, of both past and future, that both merged in my mind as a living force. A news broadcast on world-wide inflation, growing unemployment within all the industrialized nations of the western hemisphere, and a gloomy prediction for the future, had triggered off a long hidden memory of a conversation with the Brothers.

They had left me alone for some time in order that I might absorb the knowledge I had been given and commit to memory many of the scenes I had envisioned with their aid. As I began to grow impatient for the instruction to continue, they rejoined my daily meditations. It was Wen Shu who spoke first. "Having had ample time to absorb fully all earlier direction, my son, we wish to press on."

Eagerly taking the opportunity to question the Brothers once more I asked: "Can I first raise a point that has been troubling me of late?"

"But of course," he answered, his eyes a-twinkle, no doubt being fully aware of what my questions would be, yet happy to learn that I was ready to participate once more.

Taking heart from his demeanour I pressed on. "So far, the revelations have been rather gloomy, all indicating havoc throughout the world, through tidal waves, earthquakes and the flooding of the major world cities, also the collision of a planetoid with the Earth. Even so, it does seem that Man will be able to contain those catastrophies, no matter how destructive. What I want to know is: how will these situations change the race of Man? He has experienced them before and sustained them. I cannot see a purpose or a pattern. Are there other calamaties ahead of Man? How will a change in consciousness be brought about? Everything I have seen, although terrifying, can be met, without bringing about the changes you have spoken of."

Wen Shu gazed at me sadly, nodding his head in agreement. "As you say, my son, Man rarely acknowledges the lessons locked within even such great world-wide tragedies. It is only the almost total destruction of his illusionary world that will bring the remnants of the race of Man to its senses."

I gazed at him enquiringly. "What exactly do you mean by 'Man's illusionary world'?"

"I refer to the materialistic society raised by modern Man, which is based largely upon the survival of the quick witted. It is a vast illusion, a vital schoolroom for the race of Man, but sadly, the illusion has supplanted awareness of the spiritual reality and steps must be taken to redress the balance," he answered.

"But how will this be accomplished?" I asked impatiently.

Here the Atlantean interposed with: "The Ahriamanic forces, on the whole, are largely responsible for misleading the race of Man; we shall allow them to bring about the downfall of corrupt civilizations. Only in this manner will Mankind absorb the lesson fully."

I gazed at him despairingly: "Yes, yes, but HOW?"

Choosing to ignore my tone of voice he continued: "It will be achieved through the emergence of the most base aspect in Man — that of greed. There is ever greed for power, attendant wealth and the satisfying of animal lusts. Greed for power on all levels of society is the true source of evil. But . . . to be specific . . ." (he had sensed my growing frustration) "for long has the Land of the Eagle reigned supreme, due almost entirely to its gilded hoard, gained mostly during periods of great strife upon the planet. Soon the tide will turn. There will emerge those whose greed is even greater. They lust for total power, even world domination, and will be encouraged by the Great Bear to act in unison to undermine the power of the Land of the Eagle. In an uncharacteristic act of unity they will strike, and as one, they will withdraw their portion of the gilded hoard and this will greatly weaken that once mighty nation. Similarly, elsewhere upon the planet other nations held in the grip of the Great Bear will seek to loosen its hold;

great revolts will break out and these will spread as though a grass fire, setting light to many lands held for decades in servitude by the Great Bear."

He paused, then continued: "Some of these lands will then be unable to sustain their mode of life and will renege upon contracts, the burden of repayments now being too great. In the greater part this will lead to the collapse of many financial institutions in the Land of the Eagle. This collapse will be further added to as other lands, long sustained by a greedy capitalistic society, find that they too can no longer provide the means to repay the vast sums of interest exacted from them by the financial institutions.

"These situations will arise at a time when the Land of the Eagle is itself weakened through national stress. The effects of land collapse and great flooding will lead to crop failures and a time of famine within that land of plenty. The cumulative effect of these situations will lead to total collapse of the financial system, much greater than that witnessed in the past. A wave of panic will sweep the land and grip the populace, so long cushioned from hardship, and that once mighty nation will fall from its position of world supremacy, never again to regain it."

I exploded in sheer disbelief. "But monetary systems have collapsed before and nations have recovered. Why should this time be different?"

He gazed at me for some time before replying. "Because there will be a number of cumulative factors never experienced before. The Land of the Eagle lends support unto Zion and the forces of Mahomet will grow stronger. It is they who will lead the attack, sustained by the deceitful conniving of the Great Bear, which seeks to manipulate them to gain its own ends. In addition to this, the currencies of the western nations are closely interwoven, and the collapse of a major partner will lead to the collapse of all, like some great house of cards. The waves of panic will sweep the world and those who sought to gain financial benefits through the manipulation of illusionary forces will suffer a great setback. Mammon will fall. However, monetary collapse will not be the only calamity that the Land of the Eagle exports."

"Just what do you mean by that?" I queried.

"That land provides much of the world's food supplies. Reeling under the strain of major flooding in their food-producing states, the impact of the planetoid will lead to an even greater setback. Unable to sustain their supplies, famine will stalk the planet, hard on the heels of failed harvests in the majority of the western nations. The Great Bear, having by then sustained many years of poor harvests, will by force seek to wrest sufficient for its own population. In the Land of the Dragon, the rice bowls will also be empty and they too will begin to sweep into adjacent lands in their search for sustenance, their own land being ruined by earthquake and flood."

I gazed at the Brothers in dumbfounded silence, my mind trying to wrestle with the situations they had so calmly outlined. "But . . . if this happens, there will be little hope for anyone. How can anyone live through world famine and what appears to be total war?"

Here Wen Shu spoke. "No, not total war, my son, not at this point anyway, although the weaker nations will almost certainly be overrun by the stronger nations. Self preservation is the strongest impulse in Man and in the face of famine Man will do many things he would not normally consider."

He went on: "You must bear in mind that this will be a time of great change for Man; planetary conjunctions will bring about revolts on a world-wide scale. There will be a desire to express the self, free of all restriction and this, coupled with famine, will push Man to undertake that which in different times would not be contemplated. Those who have for long been held in servitude and bondage will seek to break the yoke of their masters. Revolts will occur in all classes of society. Those who organize labour will grow to greater power and will seek indirectly to rule the people, although they have never been provided with the mandate of the populace. It will be a time of the people, seeking to overturn the power of the masters. It will also be a time of political hell on earth, with those who hold power clinging desperately to it, using whatever means in their power to confuse the electorate.

"There will also arise those who falsely claim to act in the name of the Creator, false Christs who will loudly proclaim the need for freedom for all, but in turn will seek to manacle their brothers in a greater servitude. These are those who serve the Ahriamanic forces."

"Where will this occur?" I interjected.

"Look to the rising of the forces of Mahomet," answered the Atlantean. "Loud protestations and deep emotions will this evoke upon the face of the planet, bringing down the Peacock Throne, as the anti-Christ emerges from within their midst."

"What exactly do you mean by 'the anti-Christ'?" I questioned, not having met this thought before.

He answered patiently: "In the years ahead, there will arise many who will falsely claim to be the Christ and they will gather the multitudes to them. They will produce apparent miracles, which are nothing more than the manipulation of matter, some will even claim to raise the dead. They will stimulate within the unthinking an adulation, the fires of which cannot be tempered. There will also arise those who claim to be the returned Christ, returning to prevent unnecessary suffering to Man. The more erudite among you need do no more than turn to the scripture set down aeons ago, wherein it forewarns of such occurrences and the need for Man to suffer greatly before the Christ force will return. The others are nothing more than false prophets. There will eventually rise an anti-Christ who will not proclaim the fact publicly. In secrecy shall he work, turning brother against brother, until many lands are aflame."

"Do you mean this will lead to another major world war?" I asked fearfully.

"Not at this point in time, although many nations will be drawn into the conflict against Zion. At this time you would do well to observe the behaviour of the Great Bear, for it shall outreach itself."

"You speak of the Great Bear and Zion. Do you mean that Russia will attack Israel?" I asked this in almost total disbelief, for I could not see any logical reason for it.

"The Great Bear ever acts in stealth, preferring to keep its actions and motives hidden. It will use others to obtain its desires, using them to undertake the action it cannot for fear of inflaming world reaction. It searches among those lost in the wilderness, the homeless, the bitter, seeking to play upon their weaknesses. From within their midst it shall draw up a great army which will be fuelled by hatred, a force which sustains when all else goes against them. Through them the Great Bear will seek to bring about the total destruction of Zion and obtain the undying admiration and co-operation of a people, without any risk to itself. Unknown to them, it harbours designs for total world domination and absolute acceptance of its doctrines.

"At the same time, in far off India, it will be working upon the currents of fear which prevail there in order to extend its empire, and its forces will sweep through that land like a knife. Prior to that, its peoples will be subverted by those within their midst who have been affected by an insidious doctrine. The people will be tested as never before, the old and decaying will be swept away, but new life will emerge."

Here I interrupted. "Do you mean that India will be overrun and be converted to communism?"

Before answering, he gazed at me thoughtfully. "The land will be penetrated by a force seeking to subvert the people, but no, communism shall not rule in that land, the inner faith of the peoples is too deep rooted. It will bring some positive changes, however, and shake the people from their lethargy, leading to positive growth from that point on. No country may seek to subvert another by force alone. There has to be within that land the seeds of change, the insidious dark threads which are woven into the minds of the populace, working upon that which is base in their characters. Utilizing these weak vessels, forces such as the Great Bear are able to manipulate the people to their own ends."

Wen Shu then took up the tale, noting my deep interest. "India shall not be alone in feeling the onslaught of the Great Bear, my son. Other lands adjacent, indeed, once part of it, will also feel the fiery breath of the Bear. For a number of years it will infiltrate and at a time of upsurgence of belief in Mahomet, will seek to divide the people amongst themselves. Wherever a people is kept in oppression, either by their own kind or by others, the fires of change burn steadily, awaiting the wind to fan them into an inferno. But the march of the armies of the Bear will be rebuffed in lands where they encounter stiff opposition among a people sustained by Mahomet. In bleak mountain passes they will count their losses, fighting an army which appears out of nowhere, ill-equipped, but sustained by faith.

"In its determination to seek total world domination it will endeavour to manipulate the forces of those lands in which Mahomet reigns supreme. With an apparent ease the combined forces will be launched against Zion, seeming to overcome all but the most stubborn opposition. In its eagerness to settle old scores it will turn its fury against the land of the Ancient Mysteries, but the Brotherhood of the Prophet will turn against them and the Great Bear shall suffer a resounding defeat, retiring to lick its wounds."

The manner of telling this tale — largely in symbolic manner — confused me, although my long studies in the Halls of Learning during the sleep state had taught me to translate such tales. The answer lay deep within the tale itself, but locating it posed quite a problem. The Atlantean Teacher took up the tale once more.

"During this time," he said, "there will be great earthquakes in the land of Zion and the people will flee to the mountains for safety, even those mountains which have always been regarded as insecure. From those points they will regroup their armies and turn upon the invader with renewed ferocity. With the aid of the continued earthquakes they will annihilate the invaders and it will take them many months to clear away the dead."

"Will that then be the end of the warfare?" I asked hopefully.

"No," was the ominous reply. "Throughout the entire planet the seeds of war will take hold, in every land the desire for freedom — of choice — of expression — will be uppermost in Man's mind. Accepted doctrines will be cast aside, stable governments overthrown, chaos will erupt on every level of society."

I swallowed hard, quite unable to accept this unpalatable news. "There . . . does not appear . . . to be a lot of room for hope," I answered dolefully. "What will be the final outcome?"

Wen Shu drew close to me, understanding my feeling of desolation. "In all levels of society, Man will be responding to the planetary forces whose pull will be so strong that they will not be able to withstand them. These come to help overthrow the outworn doctrines and bring fresh growth, based upon a clearer understanding of purpose. Those who respond to the energies of the new Age will emerge triumphant, will become the new leaders. There is much hope for Man, a positive future, but it will not be attained without effort."

I was lost in thought, my whole demeanour woebegone, when the Atlantean Teacher snapped his fingers to regain my attention. "The physical changes in the Earth's crust, which take place during the 1980s — the earthquakes, volcanic eruptions and tidal waves set in motion by these — will merely be a preamble to that which lies ahead of Man during the last decade of this century. Then even greater turmoil will be experienced as some lands vanish for ever beneath the waves and new lands surface. The face of the planet will undergo a drastic change."

"What of my land, what of England — and Europe — what of them?" I asked anxiously.

Gravely he answered: "Your islands, long protected by the Brothers of Light, will also undergo upheaval. In the west, the coastline will rise high above the waves and the eastern coastline will sink in places, deep below them. It will be stricken with earth-shakings the like of which it has never known. The northern lands of the Norsemen and also those of the Valkyrie will undergo great change, losing much land to the oceans. The Land of the Mermaid shall separate from its neighbours and become eventually a small island, with the need to relocate its capital. There will be a great loss of life, but those aware of the impending disasters will have long fled to the points of safety."

As I pondered upon this latest revelation, the Brothers silently took their leave and I was once again alone, with knowledge so shattering that it was scarcely believable.

Chapter 12

I sat gloomily contemplating the recent memories. How had I

ever got myself into this predicament? Certainly not through conscious choice. Throughout my life my only desire had been to help others in some manner, but the role of the prophet of doom did not sit easily upon my shoulders. Even though I realized that much had been given to me over the years and was now beginning to come to pass, there was still a stubborn streak within me that refused to accept the unpalatable notion, that only through the destruction of that to which he had become accustomed, could Mankind find growth. I mused that there must be an ostrich-like outlook in the majority of Mankind when faced with such enormous considerations, for here was I behaving in a similar manner — burying my head in the sand and hoping it would go away.

Pondering on Wen Shu's various comments over the years as to my spiritual qualities, I tried to find a path whereby I could serve Mankind and perhaps avoid this unpleasant task which stared me inexorably in the face. Casting my thoughts back, into my mind came memory of a time when I met Wen Shu during the sleep state, and we spent quite an amount of time discussing the visionary experiences to which I had been recently subjected.

He had gazed at me benevolently, placing his arm affectionately around my shoulders. "There is so much for you to undertake during your current mission on the Earth plane, my son, that it becomes vital that we speed up the review of your past. Usually, such action is only undertaken when you have completed a sojourn in the plane of matter, in order that you might more readily plan for a return at some future point in time. With such vast changes ahead of Mankind, much that is not normally undertaken in the state of Earth-consciousness must be undergone. This will aid you in acceptance of the tasks which lie ahead of you."

"I have strange premonitions at times," I answered slowly, "that much which I have undergone before will overtake me and that I must be stronger this time round." I looked at him searchingly, hoping to locate an answer within his eyes.

He merely smiled as he rose to his feet. "When the time is right my son, you shall know all." With that we walked towards a small temple of Grecian design wherein sat a number of familiar souls, all clad in simple white robes.

Patting my shoulder he added quietly: "Your Teachers await; it is time for me to take my leave of you." So saying, he simply vanished from view.

Some time afterwards I was again summoned to my place in the churchyard, although by now the weather had become rather chill and not at all suitable for lengthy out-of-the-body experiences. Seemingly, Wen Shu had anticipated this fact, for he led me towards the small chapel near by, where we sat in a dim corner, unlikely to be disturbed by anyone.

"It is time to take you forward a little in time. Following the life as Mneb-Ra you made two fairly swift and short sorties into the world of matter, endeavouring to make amends for your earlier actions. Both were in the female form and produced little of note, and therefore we shall not dwell upon them. Following a stay in the realm of reality, you again chose to return, this time in the male body, returning to the continent of Atlantis as a member of the Akhadian race, which had its capital in the land of Zen-Argos. Here you trained as a physician in the Fire Temple and I wish you to take note of this brief but vital lifetime." Here again he bent over me, repeating the familiar practice of placing his hands upon my Crown and Brow Chakras, and I drifted into a state of inner consciousness.

As I regained consciousness I found that I was clad in a long white robe, having upon my head a head-dress of heavy golden metal which enclosed my head tightly, rising to a curved peak high above the crown. I found myself striding purposefully through a building with white walls which were radiating light. The light appeared to come from the actual stone itself. I soon entered a room where there were a number of men and women either seated upon, or lying upon couches. The walls in this room were strange. Large circular crystals which emitted rays of every hue were set into them and each of these projected a powerful light, the vibrations of which created a tremendous healing energy.

This was the reorientation room, where those who were afflicted either physically or mentally would undergo a balancing of their natural energies. I busied myself among those seated along the far wall, checking the individuals in a clinical manner, noting improvements upon a wax tablet near them. Stopping before one man whose eyes were glazed, seemingly quite unconscious of what was going on around him, I leaned down and spoke to him.

"Come on, Zoron, this will not do; you must endeavour to co-operate with the rays, you cannot expect us to do it all for you." The man gazed at me with lifeless eyes, making no comment, although it was evident that he had heard what I had said. "I think a spell in the fire chamber would perhaps restore you to a greater state of consciousness," I said, making a suitable note upon his tablet. "Tomorrow we shall escort you there." I moved on, noting that his demeanour had not changed because of what had transpired between us. The fire chamber was a last resort, in which the most determinedly obdurate individuals were placed to undergo bombardment with energies guaranteed to alter the outlook of even the most negative of beings.

The Fire Temple within which I served embraced the healing of the mind and body, in addition to tending to the spiritual well-being of the populace and was built within the body of an active volcano, the energies of which we controlled. From it we drew the energies to heat and light our city, in addition we channelled the gases emitted by the volcano, the purifying fire, and the cleansing waters from the mineral streams and geysers within the mountain, to sustain our healing work. Here I worked as an acolyte, undergoing different levels of initiation and training to become a physician. Passing a polished metal sheet I gazed at my reflection and gauged myself to be in my mid-thirties, fair-skinned, with straight features, and of medium height.

Many of the priests were of a great age, although their physical forms were without evidence of weariness. Our people learned to sustain the form for as long as they wished to use it, as had our forebears. It had become clear quite early in our development that it was far better to remain with a physical form for some six centuries if we wished to obtain positive results. In this manner we might take form-experience to the highest possible level. Considering the age of most of those around me I could be considered a relative youth. So far I had reached the fourth stage of Initiation and was currently awaiting training for the fifth stage wherein I would be given much more difficult tasks within the chambers of the volcano, ensuring that all of the ducts and pipes were working correctly. In certain parts, the temple was more like a great engineering station, dependent as it was upon the energies of the volcano. It was vital for the priests to understand exactly how the system operated and to play their part within it.

Among my current duties was the tending of the Sacred Flame within the temple itself. This was fed by gases piped directly from inside the mountain and a strict control of those gases was vital, for the flame must never be allowed to diminish. One day, noting that the flame was not at its usual height, I drew the attention of an elderly priest to it. He immediately grabbed me by the arms, whirling me round with a strength born of panic. "Quickly, you must enter the inner corridors and check the valves. Something must be blocked . . . ." As he spoke he pushed me rapidly towards a small door.

I tried to break his hold, gasping out, "But I am not allowed in there . . . ."

He took no notice, saying breathlessly: "Nonsense! I am too old and my eyes are not what they were. *You* must tend to the matter." With that, he thrust me firmly inside the door and shut it with a resounding bang. I heard the lock click into place and knew that I was trapped inside.

Trembling, I moved forward, but being totally unused to the maze of tunnels within the mountain, I stumbled and fell in trying to locate the source of the blockage. I very soon lost my sense of direction and the gases which permeated this portion of the temple made me feel very drowsy. Panic rose within me, knowing that I was totally lost. "That fool of a priest . . ." I mumbled to myself. I stumbled on, becoming weaker and weaker from the effects of the gases. Before I knew what was happening I stumbled against a pipe; losing my balance I began to fall and felt ahead of me an intense heat, although I could not focus my gaze clearly upon its source — within seconds I pitched head-first into the volcano itself.

I awoke screaming, the terror still very real, trembling and unable to catch my breath. Wen Shu stood close by and comforted me. "It is over, my son, over. Take a deep breath and return completely to the present time."

Gradually my panic subsided and my breathing returned to

its normal level. "Why? Why?" was all I could mutter to my mentor, the horror of the recent experience all too vivid in my mind.

"There are many reasons for its revelation, none of which would make much sense to you at present. That unfortunate priest never overcame his remorse and soon abdicated the physical form in order to meet up with you again in the higher realms. Later you were drawn together in order that he might repay his debt.

"It also indicates your starting point as a spiritually aware being. What was commenced during that lifetime must be completed during your current life experience, for nothing may remain unfinished; you must at some point in this life recreate the Healing Hospice of the Spirit as you knew it then. You must also rekindle the eternal flame of hope and compassion within your fellow Man, seeking to inspire within all the knowledge and love which comes with Cosmic Truth.

"Time is short and the Age is passing into chaos once again. As the high principles and achievements of the Zen-Argoans became corrupt and debased, they were led to a point where their civilization was wiped out as though it had never existed. The scientific, materialistic society you inhabit today is in a similar state, and those like yourself who have seen the rise and fall of many proud civilizations, will assist in combating the negative forces which once again threaten your planet. Now you must return home and rest awhile. We will meet again soon."

Gradually he began to fade from view and I was left alone within the dim chapel to regain a modicum of peace.

Chapter 13

For many weeks I concentrated on the information which had re-presented itself, trying vainly to find a pattern, and above all to find a sane reason as to why I had been chosen as one who must make these revelations. Going over in my mind the different lives which had been revealed, one point stood out. I always appeared to be serving one element — that of Fire. A life as a Fire-Bringer; another as a Fire Guardian; as Mneb-Ra I had set light to the continent with my desire for power; later, I appeared in the Fire Temple, only to be consumed by the fire itself. In my current lifetime I was a double fire-sign, indicating that I was still serving the same element, despite the passage of time.

As I pondered, I wished I could have Wen Shu with me to question, for there were so many questions left unanswered. A moment later, much to my astonishment, my spirit mentor began to build up at my side. "You are getting to be like a Genie, except that I do not have a magic lamp!" I exclaimed humorously.

"Oh yes you have, my son — your mind bids me to your side!" he answered smilingly. "Now, what questions would you like me to answer?"

"Your power to read my mind never ceases to astonish me," I cried. "However — as you ask . . . . Our friend the Atlantean spoke of the anti-Christ. Although I now understand the term, I am still a little confused. Can you be more specific, particularly regarding the manner in which this being will appear?"

Making himself comfortable at my feet, he beamed at me to show his great affection and then began speaking. "Firstly you have to realize that as the new Age begins to make itself felt, the great majority of Mankind will begin to respond to its mental energies. On all fronts there will arise a dissatisfaction with accepted creeds and dogmas, which after all are but Man-made edicts in a God-made world. At the same time, the forces of Ahriaman will begin to make their presence felt. They will seek to subvert truth and reality, and around the globe will arise many who in one manner or another will proclaim themselves to be the returned Christ. In turn, they will seek to control the minds, the emotions, and even the physical forms of their followers. Many sects will appear which will attempt world domination through their followers and will not be averse to the use of dark forces to obtain their goal."

"But surely, no one would be foolish enough to heed such teachings?" I protested hotly.

He smiled gently. "It is to be hoped that they would not, but when all appears dark, Man clutches at straws in the wind. Besides, discerning the false prophet is a necessary step towards Initiation and eventual self-mastery."

I ruminated on this, then asked: "Are there other forces or organizations we should be aware of?"

"There will be a great number, my son. For many centuries one specific group has plotted eventual world domination through the control of global monetary sources," he replied.

"For centuries?" I said in almost sheer disbelief. "No idea or dream could sustain the test of such a time scale."

His face was bland as he answered: "It can, if it is handed from father to son, as indeed it has been."

This was news of a different kind to me. "Are they working towards this at the present time?" I asked tentatively.

"Yes, indeed they are. They are most astute and their tentacles extend into the ruling factions of the major nations upon your planet. Greed is the key, and by stealth, their true purpose hidden from view, they are currently welcomed as a source of monetary stability," he said.

I sat deep in thought for some time, pondering on his words. "Will they succeed?" I finally asked. "After all, you have already indicated the collapse of world monetary power — will they not also be swept away?"

He merely smiled wisely as he answered: "They persuade Man with promises and paper, whilst they hoard precious metals. No my son, they will not be so easily overcome."

Although I had more than sufficient food for thought, I returned to questioning him once more. "The anti-Christ — will this be a singular person, a series of false Christs, as you seem to indicate, or will it be a collective belief — a point which I am coming to consider?"

Looking unusually serious for him, Wen Shu replied: "It will be an admixture of all three, my son. Just as the race of Man feels that he has rid himself of one evil, then another will appear, more noxious than the former."

I was more than a little shaken by this news, wishing in a way that I had not asked for it. "Can . . . can you . . . be a little more specific?" I asked hesitantly, not at all certain as to why I did.

"Certainly my son. Make yourself comfortable and do not fear to hear the answers that you seek." He smiled at me before continuing.

"Two collective beliefs will spread throughout the world, seeking to dominate, both inflicted through sheer tyranny. One will be the upsurge of Mahometism which will result in a baptism of fire in many European countries. In opposition to this, the cult of communism will also seek to overcome all before it.

"True communism has much to be said for it — spiritual communism, that is. The banding together of a people in communities who devote their entire energies to the members therein, all being equal. The Master of your current Age emerged from just such a life style and it was the thought that they might also have to give up all their hard earned wealth that turned many of the Hebrew community against Him and His followers. In a similar manner, the Western hemisphere recoils in horror from the current form of communism. Sadly, this has little to commend it, for its leaders are as corrupt as those of the Western nations, having little true insight into the needs of their peoples."

I had not bargained for a dissertation on the virtues — or otherwise — of communism, and held my tongue, not wishing for more of the same.

"The series of false Christs will emerge, as has been said," he continued, "but there will finally appear one individual whose charisma and personal magnetism will be such that he will succeed in misleading even the highest in the land. This, the seventh anti-Christ, will test the race of Man as never before, bringing upon the planet such a depth of suffering that many will pray for death."

This final prognostication left me completely dumbfounded as Wen Shu withdrew, leaving me to sort out my medley of thoughts.

F

Chapter 14

Deciding that I had been assimilating too much gloom and doom, I packed a case and left to spend a few days by the sea, returning to a spot where I had spent a year or two in my teens following the break-up of my parents' marriage. Determined to live and be just like everyone else for a time, I resolutely pushed from my mind everything relating to the past, feeling the need for fresh air and a calm mind. A day or two in familiar surroundings soon blew the cobwebs from my mind, helping me to assume a more positive outlook upon life. On the final day I returned to a lonely leeward shore, which had replaced my old haunt in the churchyard as the point for communication with Wen Shu.

As I wandered along, exulting in the solitude and the stinging force of the on-shore wind, my mind began to travel back in time to some of the scenes which had been re-enacted there. It almost seemed as though the past was back again and I was once more a shy, awkward boy of fourteen, finding solitude amid the seaweed strewn shore. Finding a spot to shelter from the wind, I was soon lost in scenes of the past.

Wen Shu sat beside me upon the rocks, gazing for a time at the pattern of the waves as they fell upon the shore. Turning, he spoke quietly, his gaze full of compassion. "To ensure that you realize the need for humility and strength of spiritual purpose, it is necessary for us to reveal to you a further series of lives in which you failed to make the progress predetermined for you. I will take you back into a number of experiences within which thought, used destructively, created many problems which you have long battled with, for they have followed you, life after life."

My heart sank at his words. The life as Mneb-Ra had been more than sufficient for me and the thought of reviewing further destructive lives gave me no cause for joy. Grimacing at him, I nevertheless waited for him to continue, knowing that it would be for my ultimate good.

"Following the extinction of the Atlantean continent, you were given another opportunity to overcome the temptations that come with power. You chose to reappear within your old tribe, the Turanians, who had by now become the Aztecs on the South American continent. They were a savage race which succeeded in totally vanquishing the now placid remnants of the Toltec race which also dwelt there, something they were never able to achieve in the Mother continent. Incarnating into the ruling family once more, the way was open for you to become the Chieftain, but this did not satisfy you, for you also sought the power of the Plumed Serpent." At this point he leaned across me, performing the now familiar rite and my head began to reel as I succumbed to the force of light and slipped from consciousness.

I found myself gazing upon a scene which evoked a sensation of fear within me. In a clearing amidst thick forest, a pyramid-like temple was built in stepped formation around what must have been a hilltop at some point in time. The energies emitted from this construction were hardly harmonious. Affixed above its great door was the sun's disc fashioned from beaten gold, radiating light to every portion of that clearing.

At the top of the grand stairway which ascended the almost sheer side of the temple stood a great altar stone, gathered around which were priests in varying robes, each indicating their level of initiation. Before the altar stood an imposing figure, naked to the waist, whose face and body were daubed in a multitude of colours giving a sinister appearance, completed by an imposing head-dress composed of enormous feathers. Arms outstretched, he loudly invoked energies from invisible realms.

Soon the figure of a young girl, scarcely more than fifteen, stumbled towards the steps. She appeared to be deeply drugged and showed no outward signs of fear as she slowly ascended the stairway which led to the altar. The oddly garbed priests around her gave vent to strange rhythmic chants as she did so. On reaching the pinnacle she knelt before the High Priest who effortlessly swept her up and placed her upon the altar. A swift movement removed her flimsy garment and he began once more to resume his chanting. The air became filled with an unknown energy and the atmosphere permeated with an unpleasant odour. The priests around became tense as the chanting began to reach a crescendo.

Seizing a large knife the High Priest swiftly cut the heart from his pliant victim, whilst the priests filled the air with cries of exultation, drowning the shrieks of the victim herself. Arms outstretched, the still quivering heart of the hapless victim in his hand, the High Priest shrieked out an oath to his satanic master. His eyes glittered with an evil light and it was with horror that I realized that the figure at the centre of this grim spectacle was none other than myself.

The revulsion I felt at my part in this scene swiftly brought me back to a state of consciousness and the compassionate gaze of Wen Shu. Quite unable to speak, I gazed at him imploringly, wanting to understand just why it had been necessary for me to endure that grim aspect of my long gone past. In answer to my unspoken plea, he said quietly: "During that lifetime you again contacted the dark forces and with their aid sought to dominate all about you, mentally and physically. You had been allowed to return to your old tribe in an effort to free yourself of the allegiance to the Ahriamanic forces, acquired during the lifetime as Mneb-Ra. However, once enmeshed in matter, certain memory patterns emerged and you sought to recreate them, though admittedly upon a much smaller scale. Within that lifetime you sank to even greater depths of depravity. In repayment, you swiftly returned to the Earth to find incarnation within the female form in an Aztec tribe. This was a short and terrible life in which you ended upon the sacrificial altar. The law of Karma is just; that which you sow, you must one day reap."

I was too stunned to speak, thankful that I had at least been spared vision of that lifetime.

He continued: "Your knowledge of the Lords of Power of the Left-Hand Path, of their summoning, allegiance and control, are still within your subconscious, although now there is a determination never to be drawn into that field of service again, for you have long since mastered that part of the self which leant toward the black arts. None the less, in addition to aversion, you retain a healthy respect for those who serve the left-hand path and during this current lifetime will always recognize those who follow it."

Regaining my power of speech, along with control of my senses, I ventured to ask a question: "You spoke of other lives in which I made repayment. Were there more in a similar vein?"

My hopes of not learning of any more detrimental ones were dashed at his reply. "Indeed there were; if you have sufficiently recovered, we shall continue." He gazed at me in a kindly fashion, knowing full well the effect the recent revelation had imposed upon me.

"Yes . . ." I said falteringly, "let us continue."

Wen Shu paused a minute to ascertain whether I was sufficiently recovered to hear more, then began to relate the next portion of my past.

"Once again you chose to experiment with the male form, selecting lessons which would intensify the awareness that wealth and power were not everything. This knowledge was imprinted upon your subconscious, but you needed to refresh your memory — and to repay a portion of your Karmic debt. Here you chose to incarnate within a Hebrew tribe which was eventually enslaved by the conquering armies of the Pharaoh."

Gradually a scene began to unfold before me. All around me was a huge flooded tract of land which had been inundated by the rising waters of the Nile. A large group of slaves was bent over the task of dredging up mud from the depths, and the formation of bricks. As far as I could note, I was quite young, certainly not yet out of my teens. The expression upon my haughty features was one of ill-disguised rage and resentment, my movements deliberately slow as I glowered at my captors. Despite the rigours of an almost intolerable task coupled with food which we would not have fed to our animals, my resentment still fired me to a degree of almost outright refusal to co-operate.

Noting that my speed was not sufficient for his liking, a guard brought the lash down many times upon my back and buttocks. I glared at him defiantly, longing for the chance to free myself from my fetters and teach him a lesson. 'One day I would teach these dogs who was master . . .!' A renewal of the lash caused me to lose my balance and end head-first in the murky waters of the Nile. Behind me, firm hands pulled me to my feet and I heard a whispered plea to co-operate. The guard towering over me glowered at my companion and in order to save him punishment, for his kindness, I reluctantly continued with my task.

As weeks lengthened into months, I simmered, growing daily more resentful as I grew physically weaker. Coming from a proud tribe wherein I was more or less master of my own destiny, I refused to co-operate or to bend to the lash of the whip. Many times my companions took great risks to themselves in order to save me further punishment, but I would not heed their pleas for me to co-operate.

"Never — never!" I snarled, crouched in the corner of the abysmal shelter that was allotted to slaves. "One day I will show them — one day!"

In my mind was the determination that one day I would be as them and would show them who would be master. This, more than anything, sustained me during two miserable years of intolerable hardship. My obvious resentment and refusal to co-operate led me to receive many floggings and less than my due share of the pitiful slops they fed to us. The continued ill-treatment finally took its toll and brought to an end that pitiful lifetime, my emaciated corpse being fed to the crocodiles of the Nile Delta.

As the scene faded, I gazed uncomprehendingly at my mentor, for I was bewildered as to why a life of abject failure should be brought forward. "No, my son, not a complete waste of time," he smiled, reading my thoughts. "That experience was deliberately chosen, under the fire sign of Leo, for within it your task was to come to terms with the negative aspects of that sign. However, outraged ego, resentment and frustration were prominent within your character, out of which you created a totally unnecessary return to the world of matter. Emotion, out of control, often forges links with the realm of matter which are not a part of our Cosmic learning pattern. If Man could learn this lesson, much unnecessary suffering could be saved.

"You swiftly reincarnated within the Egyptian race, this time in the female form. Like the slave experience which preceded it, this one could not be called a Karmic success, since you were not at ease in the occult, but not altogether desirable, culture of that time. Once again you returned under the fire sign of Leo, and sadly, all of the negative aspects of that sign were well to the fore within your character. You were selfish and tended to be self-indulgent and possessive, whilst making no conscious efforts to redeem yourself.

"Possessed of an artistic talent, you tended to be rather creative and also endowed with a sense of humour that today would be called cynical. Although fond of children, whom you cared for in groups in an educational capacity, you soon tired of that responsibility for it became tiresome and a burden to you. You wormed your way out of that very gracefully, being aware of the need to project a positive front to the outer world. Later in that life you married and bore two sons. The family business was concerned with the caring and training of serpents for use in the temples. Using your artistic abilities you set about creating serpent head-dresses for your family and friends.

"Over all, not a success," Wne Shu said sadly: "but hopefully you have by now learned those lessons well. You are once more back within the fire sign of Leo and need to control all negative character aspects of that sign this time around." I chose not to comment, being more than overcome with a sense of shame and failure.

"However, we have not finished yet with the negative aspects of your past." His words shook me out of my self-indulgent reverie. I looked mutely at him, wondering why I was being subjected to these unpleasant reviews. "This time I wish you to participate in the experience," he went on: "for there are still some lessons to be absorbed. From this life there are debts still outstanding." A feeling of desolation swept over me at his words; my ego was taking quite a battering this day.

Bidding me to free myself from self-pitying thoughts, he made the usual passes over my upper Chakra points and slowly a scene began to unfold before me. As it did, the voice of my mentor supplied the narrative. "This life was undertaken in the continent of India, where you were the ambitious elder son of a wealthy merchant. Upon his demise you hastily stepped into his shoes, eager to consolidate your new found empire."

The scene before me had an air of opulence about it. The place I found myself within was not a palace, yet the trappings of foolish grandeur were abundant.

"This had been your father's home, to which you steadily added items of a costly nature," continued Wen Shu. As I gazed I saw a stocky, fleshy individual, with somewhat sharp features, the ferret-like eyes darting hither and thither. This was myself, I soon realized, as I paced back and forth in eager anticipation. My wife was about to give birth and the soothsayers had assured me that this time she would present me with a son. I already had two daughters, which I considered useless to me — nothing but a drain on my finances. I needed a son to carry on the empire.

I stopped to gaze at my image in a small polished mirror, vainly preening, turning this way and that, adjusting my turban and smoothing my neatly trimmed beard. This was interrupted by a loud wail coming from above stairs.

"My son! — my son!" I shouted eagerly, waddling and panting my way to the upper level. Bursting into a large room at the top I swept aside a servant who was busily attending to my distraught wife. "Well," I demanded, "have you borne me a son?" All was silent within the room, even the child ceasing its cries. My wife stared at me imploringly. "Is it a son?" I shouted, shaking her.

She began to weep and shook her head. "It . . . is . . . a fine daughter."

My eyes bulged as I glared at her in disbelief. "Another daughter — you have failed again!" I raged, my face deeply flushed with anger. "I need a *son* . . . ." At this I stormed from the room, leaving my wife in agonized tears, for I was careless of her needs, feeling only my own sense of disappointment.

From that time on I devoted the remainder of that lifetime to the expansion of my empire. That at least did not let me down, for it grew and expanded at an amazing rate. I engaged in the purchase and sale of items large and small, no bauble too base, no prize too rare. With the Maharajas I dealt in trained elephants, Chinese silks and precious stones. On the darker side I traded in opium and trafficked in slaves. If there was a profit to be obtained, I sought it eagerly. With the proceeds of my enterprises I enjoyed my shallow, empty life to the full, particularly the power that my wealth brought me.

Although my wife adored me, I treated her with contempt for denying me the son I prized above all. My daughters I ignored, casting them aside, having no room in my life for them. The passing years brought me great power within the local Hindu hierarchy, where, solely due to my wealth, I attained the position of Patriarch. Many sought my favours, all of whom I rejected, despite the fact that it lay within my power to grant their wishes. Profit and pleasure were my goals and in seeking to fulfil them I created circumstances of hardship within which many others had to work out their destinies. My death, due almost entirely to over-indulgence, came in my fiftieth year and my unfortunate wife, despite my rejection of her, loved me still and happily committed suttee on my funeral pyre.

As this vision faded, my sense of remorse at my abject failure in this, and in all of the lives shown to me, left me with no valid comment to pass. Noting how discomforted I was, Wen Shu placed his arm around my shoulders to comfort me. "Sad failures my son, yet you will be stronger for the awareness of them. You will not, I feel certain, make the same mistakes again." I shook my head vigorously, still unable to comment.

"The latter life was one of self-seeking and self-indulgence, within which you completely ignored the persistent inner voice. This led you to suffer from all manner of minor ailments, created solely by the disharmony which existed within the self. There was a fitting sequel to that lifetime . . . ." Wen Shu paused. I gazed at him, wondering what was coming next. "Upon your demise, your three daughters and their respective husbands divided your empire equally between them, and within twenty years they effectively brought the whole to ruin. Your worldly glory lasted but a moment, then passed into the Akashic Record."

My mentor took my hand. "What you have seen has its aftermath and this lies before you in the current lifetime. Make no mistakes this time, my son. Share material wealth when it appears and it will multiply. Share and share it again, for if you ever seek to accumulate illusionary wealth, great will be your misfortune. Now return to your home and meditate upon the happenings of today. Commit them to memory, lest you should forget." He gave me a look of great love, which held within it understanding, compassion and strength, seeking to raise me from my depths of despair, then walked away along the shore and soon vanished from view.

Chapter 15

On my return to my London apartment, I went through my
notes and records thoroughly. Studying them closely to find a
pattern for the future, I could see little hope. So many
instances of sheer destruction ahead of Man — and no positive
clue as to how he might deal with the situations. The recent
review of my past had left me with a sense of failure it was hard
to shake off, particularly as I was aware of aspects of my
current personality which corresponded all too closely with
those past experiences. If these were still a conscious part of
me, I thought gloomily, how on earth was I to achieve growth
spiritually this time around?

At this point Wen Shu appeared at my side, smiling
sympathetically at me. "It is all very well for you to smile," I
said crossly, "but I do not find it very amusing."

"Come, come, my son, the purpose behind the revelations is
to instil into your conscious awareness the need for total
self-control. Better to be aware of your weaknesses and their
origins at this point, in order that you might deal with them,"
he said placidly.

I thought about this for a while, finally seeing — and
accepting — the sense in what he had said. "There are many
things I wish to know," I said, gazing at him.

He sat down before me. "That is why I am here, to answer
your questions. I am always happy to be of assistance my son.
What is it you wish to know?"

"Well . . ." I hesitated, "is there anything Man can do to
prevent much of that which has been foretold? Is it all
inevitable?"

Quietly he responded: "Yes my son, there is much that Man
can do — and you have chosen to incarnate at this time in
order that you might demonstrate to the thinking ones among
them. The major lesson lies in thought control . . . ."

"But . . . ." I interrupted, wanting something more positive.

He shook his head gently, then continued: "All problems
begin in the mind of Man. If Man can be taught to deal with
his thought patterns, many unnecessary situations can be
prevented. Take the emotion of anger for instance; so easily

triggered off, and once it is expressed it adds to the forces of war which surround the planet Earth, and also aids the forces of Ahriaman."

"How on earth can it do that?" I asked, completely mystified.

"The energies set in motion through anger, in thought and deed, create vibrations which can be utilized by others. In a similar manner, prayer aids peace upon your planet, for it creates a pool of light which helps to circumvent the energies of anger. Teach Man to spend part of his day healing the planet, encircling it with love and pure rays of light and much positive energy can be set in motion," was his reply.

"Heal the planet? But why? Surely Man has greater needs?" I was confused by his statements.

He explained patiently. "My son — you have been taught that the planet is a living force inhabited by the Solar Logos. If it wishes, it may shake Man off its back as a dog discards fleas. Many today pollute the planet, physically and mentally. Thoughts are creations and must be dealt with at some point in time. If the race of Man, or at least a large portion of it, can be prevailed upon to project thoughts of light around the planet, that force of light will then aid them to bring their negative and destructive thoughts under control, for that which you create in thought will return to you."

"Yes, that is all very well, but you have mentioned that many anti-Christs will arise and that the spectre of war and want will emerge in the future. These are the things many will want to avoid. Can they?" I asked.

Gazing deep into my eyes he answered: "War comes through the greed of Man; greed for power, lusting after that which they have not. If Man can be taught to use thought in a constructive manner, then those situations will not necessarily occur. After all, there are sufficient resources upon your Earth to feed all men, if those who have will share with those who have not. Sadly, in times of shortage, Man tends to hoard, lest at some time hardship should be suffered. Greed, my son, and a lack of foresight. Brotherhood of man — the message the Master for the Piscean Age sought to teach — has still not been absorbed."

"Apart from thought, what else may we do?" I asked

impulsively, almost certain that thought control was beyond many. Aware of my thought patterns, Wen Shu looked at me with a slightly quizzical expression: "Without thought control, my son, you will be fighting a losing battle!" Sensing my impatience, he continued: "But there are other ways in which Man can circumvent disaster. If you, and others like you who are aware, will but instruct your brother Man on how he might capitalize upon his spiritual assets — those qualities of the real self which he brings with him in life after life — then perhaps great steps forward might be taken."

"Exactly how do I — and others — achieve this?" I asked, somewhat drily.

"Through the use of your inner sensitivity, my son," he said, with a slightly reproving air. "Develop your inner vision in order that in the waking state you may be as clearly aware of the fourth dimension as you are of the third dimension. Learn to listen much more to the still inner voice and share the fruits with those around and about you; develop your ability to bring wholeness to your brother Man, with the healing touch; learn to become a positive example in all that you do and say."

"That all sounds very idealistic, but there are many who will not want to know or to listen. In fact, such expression will be the actions of a fool to the majority . . . ." Here I stopped, realizing that I was in a sense denying much that I believed in.

"Well, my son," said Wen Shu quietly, "do you believe it to be foolish?"

"No, no, I do not, but . . ." I stammered, at a loss to express myself clearly.

"Thought, my son — control it! If you believe and can share that belief with conviction, then your faith can indeed move mountains." His words were clear and emphatic.

"Fine . . . fine. I am happy to develop whatever talents you say I possess, but what can one man in a remote corner of the world hope to achieve?" I asked.

Wen Shu stared at me penetratingly, seeking to draw out from within me the answer he knew was there. I stubbornly refused to speak, blocking the required thought pattern, for I wanted him to tell me. "Alone, my son, not a great deal," he stated. "However, you must teach those who are drawn to the light within your auric pattern how they may become whole, for *you* cannot heal anyone. Man created the disharmony or disease, therefore Man must dispose of it by coming face to face with his own indiscretions, his negative and destructive thought patterns. You see my son, all returns to thought sooner or later! Also, you must travel, you must share your knowledge on a global scale."

I gazed at him in dumbfounded amazement. Travel was something I longed to do, but to teach, to communicate with numbers of others — this I felt totally inadequate to accomplish, far too aware of my shortcomings. Picking up the thread of my thought patterns, he continued.

"If you create a thought pattern of inadequacy, then inadequate you will be. There is need for you to become much more positive."

"How?" I asked blankly.

"We, the Brotherhood, will aid you. We will work by your side, we will impress upon your consciousness that which must be said, we will give you strength," he answered firmly.

I swallowed hard, unable to comprehend fully all that was being offered to me. "And . . . you think that this way I can do something for the prevention of unnecessary bloodshed?" I asked tentatively.

"Not alone, my son, but with an outlook of brotherhood, demonstrated in that which you say and do, the teaching will spread among the spiritually awakened and there are many others like yourself, incarnate today, with a similar task," was his reply.

"Will I meet some of them?" I eagerly enquired.

He smiled. "Some, yes. They will be your teachers, the light-bringers along the way."

I pondered awhile upon his statements. "It all seems very slow. Surely there will not be sufficient time for us to produce the positive results required?"

He smiled again. "Truth filters slowly into the mind of Man, but once instilled, it remains there. The world religions have much to answer for. In themselves, they played a necessary part in Man's growth, but in seeking to maintain their hold — and power — over Man, many truths have been eliminated and fears and dogmas substituted. He who labours in the field of truth brings an unpopular message and cannot expect a ready acceptance from the masses. However, as I have already instructed you, many major planetary conjunctions lie ahead and these will bring about the much needed change in outlook. Outworn beliefs and dogmas will be rejected as the race of Man seeks a more positive way of life."

"Then all is not lost?" I asked hopefully.

"Of course not, my son," he said. "What purpose would it serve if the race of Man and the planet were to be annihilated? These are very necessary tests my son, greater than Man has faced before, perhaps, but nothing that cannot be overcome. It lies within the power of Man's mind to reject power-seekers and those who desire to manipulate them. The many uprisings and revolts which lie ahead will of course bring down many a supposedly stable society, but in the main, they have become corrupt and must be swept away and replaced with more wholesome ways of life."

My questions for the day being answered, for the most part at any rate, Wen Shu and I fell to discussing ways in which I could develop my latent spiritual talents, and it was many hours before I resumed my normal daily routine.

Chapter 16

During the ensuing months I diligently applied myself to the daily practice of inner silence, a task I found exceedingly difficult, as the mind is not an easy force to control. With the aid of my spirit mentor I followed a pattern of light projection around the planet. After a time I found I was able to observe a ray of light projecting from my mind, and around the globe which I had visualized upon the canvas of my mind. He also taught me to share this ray of light with all the different kingdoms which make up life upon the planet itself — from the mineral kingdom, through the plant and animal kingdoms up to the devic and human kingdoms. The end product of this was a wonderful feeling of buoyancy as I began my daily tasks, coupled with a greater sense of personal fulfilment.

At this time I was also brought under the guidance of a teacher who, for a period of some eighteen months, expanded day by day upon the teachings given over the years by the Brothers. Between this soul and myself was a deep bond, yet neither of us could pin-point the part in our past where we had met before. Under her tutelage I began to develop my healing gift and expand my visionary talent. Suddenly, after years of inactivity, something positive was happening and the links with the Brothers intensified, for they often joined our weekly instructional sessions.

Into these periods of inner communion came strong visions, which slowly pieced together the jigsaw of the past and revealed in part the links I had with my earthly teacher. One day my meditation was invaded by a dark vision of the time of the crucifixion, which profoundly upset me. This rather astonished me, for my Catholic upbringing had conditioned me to this tale and it had never oppressed me. "Why did it have this effect on me?" I asked my beloved teacher, curious as to the reason. "Why did that particular scene, sad though it was, affect me so very much?"

Aileen smiled at me with wise understanding born of knowledge. Taking my hand she replied: "Because you were there, watching from afar. Settle down and I will tell you a little more of that life."

Gazing at her with intense curiosity I awaited her comments. Never before had she related anything of such a nature.

"We were both part of the Greek nation at that time," she began, "you, an extrovert adventurous young man, for whom the quiet life of our region held no thrall . . . ."

I interrupted. "But who were you? What were you?"

Patting my hand, she continued, "My name was Lydia and my trade was the sale of coloured cloth. During my lifetime I came across the secret of dyeing the cloth a deep shade of purple, much prized by the Romans. Later I became known as 'Lydia — Seller of Purple'. With the moneys gained I applied myself to charitable works, sensing a need to care for our people in whatever way I could. That is how we were brought together. You decided that the life of a sailor held more for you than merely existing within our region. I gave you the task of seeking new dyes, new cloths, anything you felt might be useful within my trade. You brought much over a number of years, before you decided to enlist within the armies of Rome."

I started at this comment. "I did what?" I exclaimed. "How was that possible? Surely they had sufficient manpower of their own?"

Shaking her head she continued: "Not at all. A nation which was bent upon world domination drew its soldiery from the conquered nations and you were one of many from our land who volunteered to serve, seeking excitement and to widen your horizon. I remember well the time you came back, proud as a peacock, clad in your uniform, hoping to dazzle us all with your new finery."

"What then?" I asked, anxious for her to continue.

"You were given a period of duty in the rebellious Kingdom of Judaea, which held down many legions of the army of Caesar. This was at the time when much dissention was rising within the people there. New and dangerous ideas were being voiced; there was one sect which was determined to bring down the power of Rome and the soldiery had to be ever on their guard at that time. From this strange mixture of ideas emerged one man who developed a great following and from a distance you observed the effect he had upon the populace. Often you were given a duty which involved you in attending and observing the happenings at these gatherings, in order that the Commanders might be kept abreast of what transpired. You observed that this man was gentle, yet at times seemed to be filled with an inner fire. At these times he moved the people greatly. Always there was a great deal of love evident within his words and his actions. The more you observed, the more you admired him.

"Sadly, others disagreed, and you eventually saw this man taken for crucifixion. As one of many soldiers on guard that day, you witnessed his suffering from afar and were affected by the emotion and all that transpired that day. Upon your next leave, you returned to your home and talked to me at great length of this man they were calling 'the Messiah'. For the remainder of that lifetime you followed the teachings He left behind, secretly searching for the groups which now gathered in His name. Later in that lifetime I myself encountered one who had sought to persecute him, but who had stayed on to become one of His greatest defenders."

"Who was that?" I enquired interestedly.

"He was known as Saul of Tarsus," she replied quietly.

I gazed at her in amazement. "You *knew* him?" My eyes grew large.

She laughed humorously, as if to negate any thought of importance on her part. "Only through association. When he came to our town, none would offer him shelter, for he was much feared by the Christian community and reviled by the Hebrew community. I offered him food and shelter and saw to it that those who needed to hear his message, did so. I was no great leader!" She laughed uproariously at the thought and we both fell to discussing this aspect of our joint past.

Many months later, a further life connection emerged from a series of deep meditations we had together, serving to put our association on a deeper level, for it illustrated the great depth of our past links. More than anything I had experienced in the past, this life illustrated just why I had to follow the path my feet were now firmly upon.

The first meditation had taken me into a brightly illuminated courtyard. The people in it were of graceful demeanour and the majority were clad in simple white robes, although here and there the bright flash of colourful Court robes were to be observed. The olive-skinned participants in this scene were darkly handsome, with beautifully coiffed hair. I myself was clad in a white robe similar to most, and my reflection in a near-by pool indicated that I was a tall slender youth of some eighteen years, with haughty features and neatly brushed dark hair tumbling to my shoulders, as was the style of the Court.

An air of peace and well-being pervaded the atmosphere as all awaited the call to the near-by temple. An undercurrent of excitement was evident among those gathered, for today we were to undergo further instruction in the new faith — the belief in the One God — which our young and gentle Pharaoh was endeavouring to expound. The sound of a single note from a horn silenced the chatter amongst the gathering and we stood silently to attention, awaiting the entrance of Pharaoh.

As he entered, Akhenaten gazed about him, looking lovingly at us all, his noble features calm and serene. Slowly we followed him in to the new Temple of the Sun. This was a

G

simple affair built out of doors, where we might clearly discern the symbol of the One God — the great Sun Disc — whilst worshipping. Set upon a plinth within the centre of the temple and approached by a series of sweeping steps carved from gleaming white alabaster, was the eternal cross, the Ankh. All took their places upon the steps, kneeling before this symbol of our faith, whilst Pharaoh began his Invocation to the One God. Although the Sun Disc and the Ankh were the physical representation of the faith, we were all aware that they were merely the outer material form of the One God Who pervaded all matter.

Unlike other temples in our land, we did not worship idols. Pharaoh taught that Aten was THE GOD, above all else. Although it was apparently necessary for some of our race to pray to the lesser gods, that path was not for us. The belief was simple, stark almost, in the light of the old religions, and the instruction on the necessity for brotherhood among men and the awareness of the One-ness within all creation taught us to look upon the old beliefs with new eyes. Since the young Pharaoh had ascended the throne, many young people mainly of noble birth, had turned towards the new faith. These were exciting times and a new city, fair and beautiful, was currently under construction adjacent to the Temple of the Sun. A major decision by the young Pharaoh ensured that this new city was constructed without the aid of slave labour, for he would not entertain hardship within his kingdom, even though he had not reigned for long.

The scene faded, to be replaced some days later with one related to physical prowess. In common with all of the same rank as myself I was expected to be able to drive my own chariot, and much skill was involved in the attainment of this ability. With a number of others I was practising my skill on the great plains which surrounded our city of Thebes. Being somewhat frisky that day my horse bolted, and I, unused to control, clung frantically to the chariot, quite unable to restrain the headlong flight. Eventually the chariot was brought to a halt by a group of soldiers who sprang upon me from the shelter of a rocky outcrop. My heart almost stopped beating and I was nearly paralysed with fear, for these were not the soldiers of the Pharaoh, but from the barbaric forces of

Assyria. Of late their raiding parties had taken to plundering our land, taking advantage of the fact that the new untried Pharaoh would not wage war against them.

I was dragged from my chariot and thrown to the ground, the soldiery ripping my simple jewellery from me, although they were unaware of the occult significance of the Cross of Life which they tore from my grasp. Although greatly afraid I endeavoured to project a calm exterior, demanding to be released, much to the amusement of my captors. So began a strange period for me, forced to walk in a long line with other captives, struggling along under the merciless sun until we eventually reached the Assyrian capital. My captors were a cruel and ruthless people full of barbaric intent. They lived by pillage and plunder, taking whatever they wished wherever they went, obtaining their chief source of entertainment through the suffering of their luckless captives.

It transpired that I had been captured by a band of soldiers in the pay of a warrior prince whose son commanded the party which took me prisoner. On learning that I was of noble birth I was separated from the mass of the prisoners, for they thought to obtain a large ransom for my return. In the following days the remainder of the captives were slowly and publicly tortured for the amusement of the populace.

The negotiations for my release were long and tedious and I was held captive for many months by the warrior prince. He and his son were curious to learn more of me and my people, and during the ensuing months I began to enjoy their company, endeavouring to share with them the teachings of Akhenaten concerning the One God. I tried to illustrate that lives of pillage and plundering would bring swift retribution, but they openly scoffed at my comments, stating that strength and might were the only qualities worth possessing. Determined to press this point home they took me one day on a lion hunt, but this bloodthirsty form of pleasure only served to sicken me, causing them both to laugh uproariously at my obvious discomfort and later sickness at being forced to observe the totally unnecessary slaughter.

The culture of force from which they sprang was deeply ingrained in my captors, and the sacrificial rites of Marduk had a great fascination for them. However, the months of persuasion began to take effect upon them, their outlook visibly changing. Soon word came that the Great Court of Akhenaten demanded the return of his kinsman, but that he refused to pay the ransom which the barbarian king demanded. In fury, the king ordered that I should die, slowly and publicly. The warrior prince and his son, now unable to fulfil his order, told me that the ransom had been paid, but that it was necessary for me to leave the city disguised as a nomad. I left on my way to freedom, blissfully unaware of the fate of my captors, and many months later reached the safety of the city of Thebes.

Meanwhile the wrath of the king at the disobedience of the warrior prince and his son knew no bounds. Although they begged to be allowed to pay whatever ransom the king expected to receive, the king refused to listen. To release a condemned prisoner was treason to the monarch and consequently their own lives were forfeit. All wives and children would be sold into slavery and all wealth taken by the king. The prince was sentenced to death by beheading, but his son was staked out on an anthill, for a protracted insect-tortured ordeal. The followers of the savage god Marduk met unpleasant ends for befriending the follower of the Sun God.

My period of captivity and subsequent release had a deep effect upon me and on my return to Thebes I chose to dedicate the remainder of my life to Aten and entered the priesthood, although whether or not this was out of gratitude for thankful deliverance, I cannot say. Following my acceptance as an acolyte I came under the jurisdiction of the High Priest, Xurenses, a tall man of commanding stature and regal countenance, who, like the majority of the followers of Aten, was the son of a wealthy family.

So began years of happy, dedicated service to Aten, wherein I underwent my training and initiation in the Temple of the Sun. During this period I was drawn into a close affinity with two young men whose features were disturbingly familiar. After a period it became clear that one of these was my brotherly adversary of old, Mnas-Ra, and although there was still a sense of rivalry between us, no animosity was apparent. Throughout our period of initiation we strove to aid each other, possibly clearing old Karmic links as the result.

My closest link was with another young acolyte who was tall, with prepossessing features and yet blessed with a very gentle nature. This was Kephrenaton, and try as I might I could not identify the deep sense of 'knowing' him, unable to resolve the context in which I could have known him. Together, we shared our hopes and dreams for the spreading of the religion of true brotherly love. The years passed and we each reached the stages of self-mastery, yet ahead lay the initiation many of us dreaded: the mastery of the lion. Our belief taught that a man must be the true master of his own thought, and our initiations up to this time had led us to the point of total self-control and mastery of the lower, animal nature. Now we would be allocated a lion which would remain with us, night and day, for the duration of this initiation.

First it was necessary for us to become acquainted with the lion allotted to us — and equally, the lion had to become acquainted with its new master. A lapse in our concentration at any time would lead to thoughts of the lower self and would cause the lion to attack and kill. Kephrenaton and I underwent this initiation together and in its duration we helped and uplifted each other under great stress. I believe that without the other, neither would have succeeded. On leaving the temple, our initiation behind us, we were accompanied by our now faithful pets. Our thought patterns were positive and steadfast and we at last began to fulfil our service within the Outer Temple of the Sun.

Our joy was short-lived, however, for in his early thirties our beloved Pharaoh was struck down by one who served the priests of Amon. So began a slaughter of the priests of the Sun God and eventually, all those who followed the belief. My bold, brave brother, priest Kephrenaton, was taken early in the debacle, for he refused to publicly forswear his allegiance to the One God. He and the High Priest Xurenses were flayed alive in the streets of the City of Aten, suffering a long lingering death, but each calling out the name of Aten, the only true God, to their last dying breath.

The Temple of the Sun was taken by storm as the forces allied to the priests of Amon rushed upon it. Inside were all the faithful, gathered to mourn the loss of our beloved Akhenaten, and all were cut down without mercy upon the steps of the temple; they died for their faith, happy to join the One God and their beloved Akhenaten. During this onslaught I was taken prisoner, being publicly indicated by one of my brother priests as a ringleader and troublemaker. In an act of contempt I refused to rescind my views in public, preferring to call upon Aten for release. I was sentenced for my public defiance of Amon and was staked out in the desert sands to be devoured by the insects, ants, scorpions and birds of prey.

The horror of my end brought me back to consciousness with a start, my body covered in a cold sweat. As I comprehended Aileen gazing compassionately at me I cried weakly, "Kephrenaton — it's you — you were Kephrenaton!"

She smiled gently at me. "Yes indeed, we have linked many times, but none so deeply as that experience. Now you know why we must once again jointly serve the One God and help to bring brotherhood and unconditional love to Man. That which was commenced in one lifetime must be completed in another."

Chapter 17

As the months passed I spent more and more of my time with my teacher, for in her I found someone in whom I could confide and to whom I could relate the strange happenings of my youth without fear of rebuttal; in addition I could share confidences on matters of a personal nature. One evening we fell to discussing a story which was being given a great deal of press coverage — the possibility of a shift in the magnetic poles of the Earth and a subsequent tilt in its axis.

Gazing at her from my favourite position at her feet, I asked: "Do you really think it could come about, Aileen?"

"Of course it could," she replied shortly, "— and it will. It has happened many times before, so why should this period of time be any different?"

I stared at her uncomprehendingly. "It has happened before? When?"

She chuckled at my consternation. "Many times, it is a matter of geological history. The poles have not always been in their current position. There are in existence maps which clearly show the terrain of the land which is now covered by the ice. They could not have been charted unless the land at that time had been free of ice."

I took some time to ponder this new outlook, for it was strange to me. "Why do you think it will occur — and when?"

She smiled at my curiosity. Rising, she swiftly produced a mass of papers from her desk. "Take a look at these."

"What are they?" I asked reluctantly, for they looked like rather heavy reading to me.

"Scientific reports on the build-up of ice at the South Pole. It has been increasing for some years now and rather rapidly, too." Pulling out another sheet she pointed out a paragraph which related to the north polar cap. "This is apparently melting at an alarming rate." She gazed intently at me. "If they carry on like that, the weight of the ice at the South Pole will cause it to tilt the Earth."

I stared aghast at this statement, for the implications were too horrendous to consider. "Let's ask Wen Shu what he feels," I said finally, not wishing to disbelieve my teacher, but feeling the need of some confirmation from a higher source.

Realizing full well the reason for the suggestion she agreed quite amicably and we sat together in meditation, endeavouring to contact my spirit mentor. In a short space of time he began to appear within the room, a happening which always intrigued Aileen. I thought little of it as by now I had become used to the ability of Wen Shu to manifest. Beaming at me he asked: "What is it you wish me to resolve, my son?"

Feeling just a little guilty at his words I blurted out: "Can you tell us if the Earth is going to tilt, and when, please?"

Glancing at my teacher he smiled in wise understanding. "Let us sit my son, for the night could be long."

When I had settled myself he went on: "As your teacher has instructed you, the Earth periodically undergoes a cleansing, brought about through the tilting of the poles and the shifting of the ice mass. This is precisely how the great animals which roamed the continent of Atlantis were removed from the evolutionary scale. In one gigantic move, many life forms were eliminated, in order that others might replace them. Over the years, the Brothers have provided you with ample evidence of great changes to come, wherein the race of Man would undergo enormous testing."

"Yes," I interrupted, "but no one ever mentioned such a drastic change. Surely it would set at naught all efforts at conscious change?"

Shaking his head in disbelief, he answered sadly: "My son, my son, you never cease to surprise me. When will you finally accept the fact that death of the physical vehicle is not the end?"

"I do," I cried fervently, rising to my feet, "but it just seems that such a great calamity would negate all action. What degree of tilt will it be, then, and where will the new poles be located, and . . .?" My voice petered out as he held up his hand for silence.

"One question at a time my son — and please be seated," he said, glancing in an amused fashion at Aileen who was quietly observing the interplay. "Firstly, it will not negate all positive action. That which Man consciously achieves during one lifetime, he will follow in a subsequent life. If that was not so, then what would be the purpose of searching for reality during any experience within the worlds of matter?" He gazed at me to ascertain if I wished to question him, and as I did not speak, feeling I had already blotted my copybook sufficiently for one day, he added: "The timing of the degree of the tilt depends greatly upon the future actions of Mankind."

Hesitating, I eventually asked: "How?"

Sombrely he replied, "Even today Man plays with a force he little understands. Some will begin to experiment in the vastness of the Arctic regions, hoping to escape detection, and one day may go too far, damaging the flimsy crust of the planet once too often. Already, the energies unleashed by the exploding of nuclear devices in the atmosphere, have set in motion a chain reaction which will be felt by future generations. They in turn will set in motion an increase in the earthquake activity, which during the latter period of this present century will claim many lives, and those children born during the final decade will bear the scourge of nuclear contamination within their bloodstream. The sins of the fathers . . . ."

My mouth dry at his pronouncements, I had difficulty in continuing the questioning. "And the degree of the tilt?" I whispered, my eyes wide with apprehension.

"As I said, my son, that depends much upon the future actions of Man. But," sensing my need for some sort of answer, he continued gently, "it is possible that the shift in the axis will not exceed forty degrees."

My eyes bulged. "Forty degrees!" I spluttered. "But that could well put the majority of the current civilizations under ice." A further thought struck me. "When?" I demanded.

He laughed aloud at my question. "For one who is so fearful of the outcome, you ask many questions." Allowing me to calm down before answering he rose and slowly paced the room. "It is indicated to take place in May, during the year 2000."

This quiet reply to my question astounded me more than anything else. "Are you sure?" I asked faintly, my eyes searching his face, hoping for a respite for the race of Man.

"I would not mislead you, my son; it is so written," he replied solemnly.

I sat in total silence for some considerable time, realizing that the calamity illustrated was one that I personally would have to endure and it shook my beliefs to the core, for no matter how deep one's acceptance of the continuation of life, the thought of having to undergo such an alarming test did little to encourage one to continue. Realizing the level of my thought patterns, both teacher and mentor sat quietly, awaiting my next comment.

Finally I asked: "Why has Man not been warned of this?"

He gazed at me thoughtfully before answering quietly: "He has, my son, many times. You are currently discussing one such warning, from those of a scientific frame of mind. As before, Man scoffs and dismisses these words, preferring to ignore them. For long has Man been forewarned. Even the Prophet Isaiah indicated that this would occur."

"Isaiah?" I asked in astonishment. "Are you sure?"

He smiled as he answered: "Why not read the passage for yourself my son, it is located in Chapter 24. Indeed, your sacred book tells much of the changes which will precede the new Age and the return of the Christ Light to the earth. Study the relevant passages, they will provide you with ample food for thought." Turning to Aileen he said, "I am certain that my son's curiosity on these matters can be resolved with your aid. I will take my leave of you both for this evening." With a courteous bow in Aileen's direction he dematerialized, leaving us to pore over the Old Testament.

We found many references to the predicted earth changes, not only in Isaiah, but also in the New Testament of Matthew; when compared to the more modern prognostications these bore an uncomfortable parallel to current happenings in the world. As I pored over the Holy Writ, I found much to confirm the information given me over the years by the Spirit Brothers. Why, I wondered, had I never before thought to look within the Bible for the answers to my questions? Shaking my head in bewilderment I rejoined Aileen in the search and we continued long into the night, excitedly locating different points of confirmation on matters relating to the end of the Age of Pisces.

The following morning as I picked up the newspaper, my gaze fell upon a report relating to the recent finds of rich oil deposits in Siberia, richer by far than any other in the world. I was about to turn to another page when my eye was caught by a report that the Russians were in fact using small atomic weapons in an endeavour to blast the oil shale deposits from the earth, so deep were they. I was shaken into wakefulness. Had not Wen Shu warned that such action in the Arctic regions would precipitate the shift in the world's axis? My flesh ran cold. The story was beginning to become uncomfortably real. But what could we do? What could I do?

Chapter 18

I sat for some hours pondering deeply upon all recent happenings, for the first time seriously considering my part in the world drama which was beginning to unfold before me. For years, the Brothers had instructed me, indicating that I had a major role to play within the future conflicts, yet I had always shut that aspect from my mind. Now, with the reality drawing uncomfortably close, what was I to do? How could I make people aware? As I asked myself these questions, I became aware that the energies about me were changing and as I looked up, there stood Wen Shu, gazing benevolently at me.

"My son," he said gently, "I note that you are now prepared to face your destiny. May I be of some assistance at this time?"

I sighed with relief. He had never let me down; without his loving attention, what would I do? "Oh yes please. Please help me to understand more clearly the role I have to play. So much has been indicated in the past, but as yet I am still uncertain as to how I might achieve the tasks I came to accomplish. All those years ago, that which you and the Brothers spoke of seemed like a bad dream, yet now it is all beginning to fit into place, like some Cosmic jigsaw."

He gazed silently at me for some considerable time, allowing me to gather my thoughts, realizing that unless I myself reached certain decisions, further comment would be without purpose.

"I want to help Mankind," I finally blurted out, "and I want to do what I can to forewarn others. How may I go about it?"

He clasped me to him in a loving embrace. "At last, my son! You have reached maturity, as I knew you would. Know then, that all which happens from this point on has its roots deep within your past; for this moment in time you have trained throughout many lifetimes — some of unbelievable hardship. From those experiences you gathered strength of character and a determination to face even the most impossible odds, knowing that it was possible to overcome them, with effort."

I glanced at him curiously. "You have never really explained the great links between us. Why do you take the appearance of an elderly Oriental? I know that it is but an etheric form which you hold, but why that one?"

He smiled in delight at my question. "Come, be seated by my side; I will relate, and you must again experience the past." Placing his hands upon my Crown and Brow Chakras he continued: "We were linked once as father and daughter in what was then termed the Middle Kingdom — you call it

China today. The period was some two hundred years
following the death of the Great One known as Confucius, and
we were together in connection with the Temple of Peace.
Sadly, it was a time of violent civil war . . . . Now relax and
observe."

My head swam in the familiar fashion and I slipped from the
present time into the long-gone past. As the mists cleared I was
within an ornate building, the interior richly decorated with
elaborate carvings; all was dark and cool. There was little in
the nature of furnishings, for the followers of the faith would
enter and take their place upon the mosaic floor, which I was
engaged in washing thoroughly. A rude wooden bucket was
filled with water, the top of which was covered with scum.
'Time for fresh water' I thought and wearily rose to my feet,
and I could see that my young frame was clad in sparse, ragged
robes which had seen better days, but which were sufficient for
the task I was engaged upon. Times were hard and due to the
continual warring within the state, the pedlars and merchants
rarely came our way; when they did, many of them were
slaughtered for the trinkets and bales of cloth they carried.

Shielding my eyes from the glare of the sun, I left the
temple, carefully disposing of the contents of my bucket upon
a near-by field. Water was precious at this time of year and
there had not been any rain for some time. I set off for the
river — now a mere trickle in the midst of the dried-up bed. If
the rains did not come soon we would all starve. Shaking my
head at the thought, I wearily plodded my way to the centre of
the river bed to fill the bucket. I knew that soon I must return
to the compound to prepare the meal for my father and my
small son, who no doubt would be up to mischief, as he was
allowed an enormous amount of latitude by his benevolent
grandfather. Oh how I wished for the end of the feuding and a
return to a peaceful way of life. I wistfully thought of my
young husband who had been swept up into the ragged armies
with brother fighting against brother — in pursuit of what? I
wiped a tear from my eye as I thought of the three brothers
and my husband torn from us, and with no end in sight.
Wearily I climbed the steep steps and entered the blissfully
cool and peaceful interior to resume my labours.

Some hours later, relaxed upon my favourite cushion I

watched my father at play with his grandson. Still a handsome figure even at his great age, Wen Shu delighted in his first grandson, and although he taught the local children, instructing them in the way of the faith, his own grandson was very special to him. "What news of the war, Father?" I asked. "It has been long since we received any communication from my brothers. And," I added wistfully, "my beloved husband."

Gazing at me keenly he commented: "No news of our loved ones, my daughter, but today we heard that the forces of Tzang-Tze only last week razed the temple to the ground in Hungchow."

I stared at him fearfully. "But that is only two days' journey from here! Will they come here? What of us, what of the child?"

Seeking to calm my fears, he put his arms comfortingly about me. "Peace my daughter, the Lord will protect us." Seeking to steer the conversation into brighter channels he said brightly: "What would my grandson like to play now?" Scooping him up into his arms, they disappeared amidst loud whoops of joy from my son.

Three days later, a horde of soldiers swooped down upon our small settlement in a storm of dust and began to kill without pause, grabbing what women they could to satisfy their lust before brutally murdering them. Wen Shu grasped my small son, who was ever curious, and moving quickly thrust me before him into our deep root cellar, which was largely empty now awaiting filling at the time of harvest.

"Hide here, my daughter, I will see what I can do for the other children," he said urgently.

I clung to him imploringly. "But Father, what if they attack you? Please, oh please stay with us."

He gently pushed me aside, pulling himself up to his full height. "I must do what I can for those who survive. Remain here, all will be well." With that he sped off into the village.

For hours the cries of fear and the sounds of butchery echoed above our heads as we huddled deep within the cellar. My son, quite unaware of the calamity outside, could scarce be stilled, fretting for his beloved grandfather. With the coming of the night I peered fearfully out, seeking to locate my father who had not returned. The occasional shrieks still rent the air amidst the drunken outbursts of the raggle-taggle soldiery. Creeping out into the compound I stumbled upon a crumpled form lying in a pool of now drying blood. I clasped my small son to me, stifling the agonized cry which rose from within me, for I did not wish to attract the attention of those who were even now rifling the compound for whatever they could find.

"Grandpa . . . . Grandpa . . . ." cried my son.

"Hush, darling, hush," I whispered fearfully, the sorrowful tears falling silently. "Come, we must leave."

"But Grandpa — what is wrong with him?" he whispered tearfully.

I hugged him to me, my tears splashing upon his upturned face. "He . . . he has . . . ." Suddenly, with a drunken roar one of the soldiers fell upon us, tearing at my clothing, his beady eyes filled with lust, yet none too steady on his feet.

Dropping my son I shouted at him to run to the cellar and then turned to wrestle with my attacker. Finding a strength born of desperation, I grappled frantically with him, causing us to trip, and as I fell upon the drunken fool I seized the opportunity to gouge out his eyes. "That's for my father!" I sobbed. Screaming with agony he lunged to his feet and lashed out at my body, felling me with one blow, causing me to fall heavily upon the ground, striking my head upon a stone with some considerable force. Reeling dazedly to my feet, anxious only to rescue my son and flee from this place, I did not heed my wound, but staggered to the cellar, where I found that my son had been crouching outside watching with fearful eyes all that had taken place.

"Come quickly, my son, we must hurry and be very quiet," I whispered agitatedly. His tongue stilled by fear he clung to me and we crept off into the night. We climbed for hours high into the neighbouring mountains, seeking to put as much distance as possible between us and the soldiers. With each step I grew weaker, now aware of the blood flowing from my head wound. Tearing off a strip of my ragged robe I bound the wound as best I could, not wishing to waste time in outdistancing our pursuers. As the faint light of dawn began to appear above the mountains we stumbled upon a crude wooden shelter set partly into the side of the mountain. A herdsman's shelter — it would give protection from the sun and also a chance for me to rest. Stumbling within I fell into a state of deep feverish sleep.

Later that day I awoke to find my son being tended by the herdsman, who had also cleansed my head wound. Smiling, he rose and came to my side. "You are awake?" he asked gently. "I thought perhaps you would not."

Smiling weakly at him I clutched my son to me. "Thank you for tending to us. The soldiers . . . ." My voice trailed off into silence, fraught with memories of the horror we had been through.

"I know," he answered, "your son told me." Shaking his head, unable to understand such actions, he set about bringing me some food. "It is not much, just a little rice," he said apologetically. "I do not store food here, apart from a small supply for emergencies."

"It is fine," I smiled, although my head hurt dreadfully and I was unable to rise, feeling so weak.

"You must rest," said the herdsman, "while I go for help."

Help did not come for some three days, by which time I was pitifully weak from the loss of blood; what energy I had was expended in keeping my small son pacified. With the return of the herdsman and his two daughters, I relapsed into a deep coma, from which I never recovered.

As I began to return to the conscious state, I gazed at Wen Shu, joyful to realize that he was still there, but distressed at the situation of my small son. "What happened eventually?" I asked tremulously.

He smiled gently at me. "The herdsman reared him as his own, and time soon healed the wounds, although he never forgot you. Indeed, you will meet him again during this lifetime, for he is due to incarnate soon."

I started up at this. "Really? Where? When? Do tell me . . . ."

"Patience, my son, patience!" Wen Shu replied in an amused tone. "When the time is right, he will recognize you, and you will be disturbed by his effect upon you."

I gazed imploringly at him. "Will we be together at some point in time?"

"Indeed, my son, but old patterns must first work out," he said. "That herdsman will provide the vehicle and will eventually give your son back to you. Many things must occur before that event takes place, however. It is sufficient for you to be aware of him and know that there is ahead of you both a time for completion of that earlier experience. As for now, I wish you to apply yourself in earnest to your studies. Your teacher has been placed upon your path at this time with such an end in view. You must consciously seek to develop your spiritual talents, acquire as much knowledge as you can. You must learn to tend your Brother in his hour of need. There are many years of study ahead of you yet — years in which you will regain past knowledge, reawaken past skills, ready for the time when your brother Man will have need of them. Time is not important; all will happen when the energies are in place."

"Thank you Wen Shu; but may I still call upon you for further enlightenment?" I asked, half fearful that he was about to desert me yet again.

"Of course my son, I shall ever be by your side. Your thought patterns will draw me in your time of need."

Greatly reassured, I fell to pondering the happenings of the last hours, not noticing the disappearance of my mentor.

Chapter 19

For some months I attended to my studies with diligence, developing my latent healing talent and absorbing the knowledge which one day I would have to couple with it in order to bring about the return to one-ness within those who sought my help. An idealistic outlook upon life began to replace my hitherto gloomy view and I began to look forward with hope to the opportunities which lay ahead, wherein I would be provided with the means to serve my fellow Man.

One day, discussing the predicted Earth changes with my teacher, I began to relate to her the happenings of an evening in my childhood, when the Brothers had joined me during my meditation. That day had been a difficult one for me for no matter how I tried I could not come to terms with the gloom set in motion by predictions which I had been given for the future. Seeking to dispel the unrest in meditation, I soon found that the Brothers had joined me and were sitting in a semi-circle around me.

The voice of Wen Shu penetrated my consciousness. "You have some points you wish to discuss, my son?" As he smiled at me, it seemed that the whole room filled with light, dispelling my fears at once.

"Yes. I would like to clarify the picture in relationship to the geophysical changes. You have indicated much coastal erosion, particularly in the Americas, and great flooding in my portion of the hemisphere. Can you tell me if there will be further occurrences?"

Wen Shu answered immediately: "Indeed, my son, there will be much more, for those already mentioned are but the beginning. The land mass in certain areas of the Americas is built upon weak sedimentary material; their scientists will soon discover this point to be true. Weakened by earth tremors, the land at these locations will collapse, allowing the seas to pour in. In turn this will lead to great tidal waves sweeping up the coasts, flooding the waterways which feed the inland lakes. This will set in motion much havoc for cities built around those lakes; few will escape the devastation — the cleansing will be thorough."

I recoiled in horror at this bland assessment. "But why?" I gasped.

He paused, eyeing me pensively before replying. "The points of gross materialism must be cleansed, the cities in the path of the destruction are those within which Mammon has assumed alarming proportions."

"Mammon?" This biblical reference left me bewildered, for what had it to do with our modern times?

"Those who seek to accumulate material excess without thought of the true needs of their brother Man, those who sow the seeds of dissention based upon colour or creed, are all serving — indeed are the worshippers — of Mammon," he said sternly.

Shaking my head disbelievingly at this, I asked him to continue. "You have also spoken of the continent of Europe undergoing great changes and particularly here in England. I

H

have always been led to believe that this land was a protected isle. Is that not so?"

He nodded gravely at me. "It has been and will continue to be, my son, for it has deep connections with ancient civilizations. However, for the past six centuries your land has been led by a succession of souls who had established themselves as pioneering tradesmen in ancient civilizations. They took your land to its peak of fulfilment, but often the power which fell to them was abused by their successors. That era is at an end.

"With the tilting of the globe, which will come about with the shift in the polar ice caps, England — in part — will undergo submergence along its eastern coastline, whilst its western coastline will rise high above the waves. Other lands adjacent will also be affected in differing ways. Another ancient magnetic point is located within that land of many windmills, currently far below the level of the sea. A courageous people, who one day will lead great portions of the world through their positive examples in education and political expertise; their land will rise dramatically above the seas, becoming elevated.

"Many neighbouring lands will be greatly affected by the subsequent flooding, but portions of the Lands of the Norseman and the Valkyrie will be saved. The Land of the Mermaid will become an island, floating alone upon the ocean. In other directions, the Lands of the Camel will survive, indeed, will expand, as will the ambitions of the people. They have much to learn and will be provided with ample opportunities to do so. Portions of the ancient kingdoms of Europe adjacent to the mighty Alps will also be saved, as will portions of France. The land divided against itself in the name of God will be safe, for it has much ancient wisdom to offer Man."

"To which country do you refer?" I asked, a little bewildered.

"That land adjacent to your own, where brother fights brother upon matters of belief," he answered.

"Do you mean Ireland?" I asked, finding this difficult to believe, feeling that the religious bigotry which existed within that land must surely warrant cleansing. Almost in answer to my unspoken thought he replied swiftly.

"That land will be cleansed of religious intolerance, for it is an ancient land and has much to offer the race of Man."

I acknowledged this comment with a quizzical look, then said: "You spoke of France being partially flooded and I have had earlier visions of great wars taking place there. Why is this?"

He paused a moment before replying, gazing at the assembled Brothers for tacit confirmation of what he was about to say. "There are many incarnate within that land who once possessed great occult power. These are extremely sensitive souls, yet they consciously choose to ignore their instinctive awareness of Cosmic Law. Instead, they follow a blind nationalism and often an equally blind faith, ignoring their chosen role in life. Without their aid, their land will fall into disarray and will have to undergo a great cleansing, in order that the conscience of the nation might once more become pure." As I gazed at him uncomprehendingly, he continued: "For centuries the people have followed lower passions and much that was pure within the land has evaporated. That which a people does, taints the nation, even the land itself. This must be cleansed in order that a new light may be kindled within it."

I thought about this, then asked: "In all this you do not say anything of Italy. Once, you spoke of great earthquakes affecting that land. What is its destiny?"

"Again, my son, it is a land where the emotions have long ruled the people and the land bears a deep taint created from centuries-old thought patterns," he replied. "The land itself will gradually sink beneath the waves, brought about largely through earthquake activity. The sea will boil for many a year and will wash over that once beautiful land. The ancient egos who go with it will return into a near-by land at a later date, and this will teach them to direct their emotionalism into precise and exact channels, eliminating the excess of destructive emotion."

The thought of the total destruction of a land and a people for whom I had a deep affection numbed my senses and prevented further logical thought. Noting this reaction, Wen Shu quietly took his leave of me and the Brothers began to fade from view, leaving my thoughts in a turmoil. Even now, as I related all this to Aileen, the horror of it was still intense. She, being of French extraction, was equally distraught at the news of that which lay ahead of her country of origin. Gazing at each other sorrowfully, we decided to close our discussions for the day and I wended my weary way home.

Chapter 20

Seated one evening with my teacher, in the quiet period which always followed our healing instruction sessions, I fell to wondering where I had acquired this strange gift and why I was being selected to utilize it. In the beginning I had been deeply sceptical of this apparent quality in my teacher; the thought that I also was to use it, at first aroused derision within me. Only the positive demonstration of the quality inherent within me, by means of large quantities of ectoplasm pouring from my hands, making them feel as if they were on fire, finally convinced me that perhaps there was something in it after all. But where had it all commenced? Atlantis perhaps? I knew from my long sessions with Wen Shu that I had served within the Fire Temple where I had undergone training as a physician. Was that the sum total of my past healing experience, I wondered?

As before, in answer to my thoughts, Wen Shu began to materialize before us, much to the pleased surprise of my teacher. Deeply amused by her reaction, he bowed graciously to her, saying: "My son — our pupil — has many questions that require an answer. I have come in order to fulfil his need."

Aileen smiled at him, her eyes twinkling merrily. "Well, it would never do for him to go without an answer, would it? Do please carry on," she said, making herself comfortable, for she was becoming accustomed to the sudden appearance of the Brothers and relished the opportunity to learn more of my past — and my future.

Turning towards me he beamed delightedly. "In answer to your questions, my son, there have been several other Earth experiences within which you trained for the healing art. They were not necessarily easy, but valid in the light of that which lies ahead of you. During this lifetime you will encounter many souls who have been involved within those earlier experiences; each will have something to offer, and in return, you will have something to teach. Now I will take you ajourneying once more into your past. Be still and I will relate as we journey back." Placing his hands upon my head in the usual manner he caused me to slip into a state of out-of-the-body consciousness.

"I am taking you back into a life in the North Americas, where you incarnated in the female form within a tribe of desert-dwelling Indians. This was a very hard existence and the majority of the tribe rarely attained middle age — indeed, many vacated the physical form during infancy." As the mists cleared I was in the midst of a small tented settlement with little natural shelter, and the sun was beating down, making the air heavy and oppressive. I was seated outside a tepee set apart from the remainder, a large totem standing a little distance away denoting the purpose of that which was undertaken within it. I was seated before a large flat stone upon which I was grinding herbs.

The voice of Wen Shu continued the narrative. "At an early age your psychic gifts were discovered by the Medicine Man, who was second only to the Chief in the tribal hierarchy, and he promptly took you from your parents and raised you as his own child. This primitive form of adoption could have been disastrous, but luckily he was a kind man, despite a stern exterior, and wise in the ways of life. You grew to love and respect him as your own father. He had two natural sons, who were uncouth and bullying, for they envied the love and affection shown to you by the Medicine Man. They had no psychic powers, which was the real reason you were adopted, for there was no natural successor to him. Now, take note."

As I sat at my task, the younger of my two brothers swaggered out. Thrusting an empty water skin at me he snarled: "Water — and be swift, unless you wish me to punish you again."

I gazed at him fearfully. "But Father asks that I complete the . . . ."

Sweeping my herbs to the dust in rage he shouted: "Do as I

say." He raised his hand as if to strike me. Cowering from him, I grabbed the water skin and scurried to the near-by spring, followed by his raucous laughter.

At the spring I bent over my task, tears cascading down my face; glancing anxiously to see the position of the sun I thought: 'Oh dear . . . I must now collect fresh herbs and prepare them. Father has need of them for the potion for Golden Wing's papoose.' I cried out in despair: "Oh why are my brothers so cruel?" I simply could not fathom why they disliked me so much. I tried so very hard to please. The skin now filled, I ran swiftly back to the tepee, not wishing to anger either my brother or my father. Thrusting the now filled skin into my brother's hands, I set off once more in search of fresh herbs, in order that I might complete the task set me by Red Eagle.

As the years passed and I grew slowly into womanhood, my father trained me in all aspects of his magical art. I looked forward eagerly to the times when we set out to spend days alone in the wilderness, where he would instruct me in the many and varied roles which fell to the medicine man. Here he taught me weather prediction, vital to a tribe such as ours totally dependent upon rainfall for sustenance. In particular I loved the language of the stars, by which he taught me the art of prediction in connection with the future, for this played a major part in tribal life. Hour after hour I would sit happily by his side absorbing his words, following his instructions carefully, determined that I would never fail him in the role for which he was training me. He also instructed me in the use of herbs and how to cast spells in cases of sickness, for our people believed that deep sickness was caused through possession by evil spirits.

Most of all I enjoyed the times he set aside for teaching me tribal lore and the folk legends of our people, for he had the knack of bringing them to life. "Tell me, Father, how did our people come to live in this harsh land?" I asked eagerly. He had told me many times before, but I never tired of the tale.

Smiling indulgently at me he answered: "Our people once lived beyond the great ocean, upon a fair land called by the name of Atlan. It was a wondrous and fair land, the climate cooler than here, with many, many trees and much pasture for the buffalo."

"Why did we leave then, Father?" I asked eagerly.

"Many great fire mountains cast much fire down upon our people; then the land opened up and swallowed many of them, so we built mighty canoes and for many, many moons journeyed across the great ocean, until we landed here. Our people wandered, always they wandered, in search of food, in search of land like ours, but we never found it, so now we stay here, moving only when the water dries up."

"Will we ever return to that land, Father?" I asked, my mind filled with his vision of a fair land.

"No, my child, our ancestors settled, we have settled; the Great White Spirit has led us here. Now we stay; this land is ours now."

One harsh summer, when even our ever-faithful spring was reduced in its supply, Red Eagle took me on a long journey in search of water, for it was now obvious that the tribe would have to move to a new locality. Gazing at me with pride as we set out he said: "Now I will show how to divine for water. It is time for you to develop your talent, for one day it will be your task."

I gasped with pleasure at this, for I was always astonished at his ability to locate water in even the most arid region. Smiling shyly at him, I increased my pace, now eager to develop this new quality.

For many days we trekked in difficult terrain, during which time he remained silent, for he had instructed me in the use of the birch twig and did not give me any indication at each of my attempts as to whether or not I was correct. Failure after failure caused my confidence to ebb away and now I could scarcely look at him, for fear of seeing reproval in his eyes. It was not a simple task, and I now fell to wondering if Red Eagle had not perhaps misjudged my apparent ability. How, I wondered, was I to know whether or not I was above the spot where the life-giving waters lay hidden deep within the earth?

Growing desperate, I set out one evening, leaving Father by the camp fire. He did not comment on my leaving, knowing full well why I did so. Once clear of the camp site I sat and closed my eyes, and raising my voice cried out aloud: "Oh Great White Spirit, let me not fail my father and our people;

guide me to the hidden waters." Continuing to sit quietly, I awaited an inner direction and when this came, grasped my twig firmly between my palms and set off at a rapid pace, a sense of anticipation growing within me.

Suddenly the twig pulled in a sharp downward direction, close beside a boulder I had passed the previous day. Try as I might I could not lift the twig to its original height. Dropping it, I sank to my knees, scooping the sandy soil with my bare hands. As I dug, the sand grew soft and moist and the deeper I dug the wetter the soil became. Stopping momentarily to wipe the perspiration from my brow and to regain my breath, I noted that the hollow was beginning to fill with water. Whooping with joy, I continued to dig, anxious to provide Father with a deep and positive pool of fresh water. As I continued my labours I became aware of a deeper shadow cast across the now growing pool. Looking up, I met the gaze of Red Eagle, and although his face was impassive I felt intense joy radiating from him.

"Father, Father, look! Water — cool, fresh water!" I cried, as I wept for joy, knowing that I had not failed him, and silently I thanked the Great White Spirit for making this possible.

One of the many roles which Red Eagle fulfilled was that of tribal medium, vital to the initiatory rites of tribal lore. In addition to this, he was also a mystic, possessing a much deeper awareness of the purpose of life than he ever shared with the majority of the tribe. He sought to develop these qualities in me, and during the long winter nights he taught me how to control my trance state. This was a dangerous task, for within these rites I would be possessed by the long-gone spirits of our ancestors, and care had to be taken that during my training I did not attract evil spirits who would seek permanent possession of my body.

This training involved the smoking of pungent herbs which grew in certain areas of our terrain, and sometimes the eating of fungus, which produced strange out-of-the-body experiences. In Red Eagle's care I was safely protected from the many traps which await the unwary seeker in the lower astral realms. For many years this part of my training proceeded until I was able to undertake the deepest state of trance, speaking in loud ringing tones, producing words of warning and prophecy for the tribal elders.

The culmination of this portion of my training came in one night of test held at the time of the High Summer Moon. This was a sacred time for the tribe, a time when the young braves underwent the greatest initiations in order that they might prove their manhood. For two days prior to this Red Eagle had instructed me carefully and placed me upon a strict fast, allowing only the partaking of the fungus during this period. At the time of full moon I was led into the sacred circle and was dimly able to discern the many faces of those gathered in the great tepee. Intermingling with the physical bodies of the braves were many apparitions of braves who long ago had passed to the happy hunting ground, for they had a large part to play within this ceremony. Any expression of fear on the part of any participant would result in great suffering.

Hour after hour I witnessed the most appalling ceremonies which tested to the full the ability of the assembled braves to withstand the frontiers of pain. Unable to focus clearly, I was constantly prodded and told to indicate that which was to be seen within the patterns of the brave concerned. Upon my visionary qualities lay the future of the assembled braves. Finally, within a rising crescendo of invocative sound which sought to call upon the spirits of past chiefs to indicate those who would go forward to lead the tribe in future years, spirit after spirit passed through my body, which writhed and cried aloud, indicating the fate of each one. Eventually I collapsed in a deep stupor, from which it took me many hours to recover.

With the coming of my womanhood, the health of Red Eagle took a turn for the worse and his growing frailty gave me great cause for concern. One day he called all his family members together and as we assembled, I felt a sense of premonition, which filled me with fear. Quietly Red Eagle spoke: "Soon it will be time for me to join my ancestors in the happy hunting grounds, for my time is almost at an end. Before I take my leave, I must ensure that our people have a strong spiritual leader." Turning to me he continued: "You, my daughter, are that leader, but I fear that the tribe may not accept you, for you are but a squaw. It is therefore necessary that you are taken as wife by one of my sons."

I paled at this news, for I had encountered nothing but resentment and cruelty from my adoptive brothers. As the tears began to stream down my cheeks, Red Eagle continued: "I select Red Wing, my eldest son, for by right he is my successor in the eyes of the tribe." My heart sank, for of my two brothers, Red Wing was the most brutal. I also knew that he had hoped to take to wife Shining Waters, and this decision of Father would arouse even greater antagonism towards me.

The arrangements were set, none asking or even interested in my views and I would soon be wed to my brother. In marriage he proved to be even more brutal, at times downright sadistic, taking great pleasure in inflicting pain upon me. For some reason he feared me and my talents, resenting the fact that he did not possess them. Brutality was his way of gaining revenge. As a submissive Indian woman I accepted my lot in silence, gaining relief only in times of tribal need. The eventual passing of Red Eagle left a great gap in my life, the only source of love and affection now lost to me.

During the ensuing years I faithfully fulfilled my role as Medicine Woman, the tribe ignoring my husband, knowing full well who it was who had the true power. Despite my gender I was readily accepted as spiritual leader of the tribe and this fact leavened a sad and unhappy life. Early in the marriage I bore a son, but childbirth took a heavy toll of my physical frame, leaving me in a greatly weakened state for the remainder of that lifetime. The continued ill-treatment by my husband in addition to my failing health caused my powers to wane and the members of the tribe sought me out less and less, seeking another to fulfil their needs. Realizing that all which I valued was slowly ebbing from me, I lost the will to live and soon joined Red Eagle in the happy hunting grounds.

As I began to regain consciousness, I found Wen Shu — who was at hand, as always — and Aileen, both closely observing me. This relieved me greatly, for the recent experience had left me feeling deeply unhappy. Wen Shu smiled gently at me. "The lifetime you have just experienced was extremely rewarding for you in relation to the Karmic Cycle. You learnt much, accepted pain and antagonism with philosophic gentleness and fulfilled your spiritual destiny. Although you did not live to see the day, your son eventually became Chief, due largely to the powers he inherited from you. He became a deeply respected and renowned leader."

As he spoke, I became aware of two shadowy figures in the background. They stepped forward slowly. The first I recognized upon the instant. "Red Eagle," I gasped. His deeply lined face lit up with joy at my recognition. In turn he extended his arm to the other figure, the sight of whom pleased me less. "Oh — Red Wing, too," I added rather doubtfully. His face grave, he bowed deeply before me, his eyes searching my face for reassurance.

Wen Shu interrupted: "The past is over, my son. Both the Brothers have selected the opportunity to serve alongside you during this current lifetime."

I gazed at all three, a little astounded, although delighted to meet up with Red Eagle once more. He stepped forward and took my hand in his. "As before, I am to instruct you in the art of trance mediumship, except that this time it is I who will be the contact within the spirit realm. We will begin the training very soon. It will not be an easy task for you, for there is none on the Earth plane who can instruct you this time around. Rest assured that I come in love and will ensure that you do not come to any harm. It is to ensure that there is a continuation of communication that this experience was reawakened within you."

I gazed joyfully at him. "And . . . Red Wing . . .?" I asked hesitantly.

"I will work alongside you in the field of healing," he said, stepping forward, "that is — if you will allow me? In the past I did not understand your powers. Now I am offered the opportunity to make amends. Will you please accept my assistance?" he asked imploringly.

Not quite knowing what reply to make I gazed around at the assembled Brothers and at Aileen, who was watching the unfolding panorama with an air of fascination. "Of course," I finally replied, "for I will need a great deal of help. Yes — I will accept your offer of assistance."

Smiling broadly, Wen Shu stepped forward. "Good for you, my son. Links once forged, be they of love or of negative emotions, cannot be broken. They must be resolved through association at some point in time. Now my son, we must not take up any more of your time." His eyes twinkled at this comment, knowing full well that I was happy to spend hour after hour in his company. Raising his hand in a salute of farewell he added: "I will return at a later date to continue the tale of your healing experiences."

Red Eagle and Red Wing smiled at me in turn, before they too took their leave of us. Soon Aileen and I were left alone with much food for thought and a great deal to discuss.

Chapter 21

For many weeks Aileen and I discussed the information which had been received from the Brothers and naturally we always returned to the matter of our own land. What exactly would happen to England? Should we make preparation, should we in fact seek to emigrate to one of the apparently safe lands? Wen Shu had warned me against that, but what were we to do? We needed more information. As usual, when our thoughts were upon such taxing matters, the Brothers made their presence known, and joined in our discussions.

Gazing at them, I asked, "Is there any further information relating to our homeland of which we should be aware?"

The Atlantean Teacher rose and gravely answered. "There is indeed much, but you have to learn to absorb it as part of your growth pattern. Endeavour to observe the Cosmic Plan for the planet working out within it, and indeed, within all we shall reveal to you. We seek not to alarm, but to strengthen. Is there not a saying in your world — 'to be forewarned is to be forearmed'?"

I nodded vigorously at him. "Yes there is, but it is far from easy to be dispassionate when those whom we love dwell in areas which are scheduled for destruction in this manner."

Placing his hand affectionately upon my shoulder he said: "You must endeavour to love all Mankind, look upon each and every one as your family, which indeed they are, for the family of Man are the children of the Father. Try not to ponder upon your genetic family, for they too have their lessons to absorb this time round."

Grasping his hand I muttered dolefully, "I realize that what you say is correct, but it is not so simple to put into effect. However, I will try."

"Good," he cried, clapping his hands together, "we shall continue our discourse on the path ahead of Man." Seating himself amongst the Brothers he continued: "We have spoken in the past of new lands arising in the ocean west of your homeland. This action will eventually have the effect of displacing the warm waters which currently flow around your coastline, keeping your climate temperate. The warm waters will be redirected and will begin to flow around the new lands as they emerge from beneath the ocean. The end result will be to reduce temperatures greatly within England and within neighbouring Europe. Before the end of your current century, ice will begin to build up within your own land, making habitation nigh impossible for all except the most hardy."

This news was completely shattering. "Do you indicate that a new ice age is about to commence?" I asked apprehensively.

Wen Shu said swiftly, before I could say more: "No, no, my son, not at all. That is where your scientists have their facts wrong. What they refer to as a new ice age indicates the shifting of the Earth's axis, which we have earlier indicated will take place at the turn of the century. Even so, areas which are presently ice-bound will become torrid and vice versa. There has never been a time when ice covered the entire planet, the position of the polar regions is merely reversed or moved to a totally different position."

Turning to the Atlantean I asked: "The new land which will arise, will the people of Europe and England move there? Is it old Atlantis?"

He nodded gravely at my questions and replied: "Yes, it is indeed a portion of the ancient land, but Man cannot settle upon it for many centuries; it will first be a place for bird life, which in turn, will prepare the way for the creation of soil. It takes aeons of time for a land to be fit to support Man. Sadly, many of your race choose to ignore this fact and seek to destroy the planet which gives them life."

I pondered upon this reply for some time. "What then are

we to do?" I asked.

He looked gravely at me. "Allow the Cosmic Plan to work out, fulfil your part as indicated. Man will be given ample warning within your portion of the hemisphere; the wise will heed and flee, those who are rooted within the third dimension, placing greater emphasis upon worldly goods and possessions will remain to work out their Karmic debt."

Wen Shu, feeling the need to lighten my mood, stepped forward. "It really is time to extend your conscious awareness, my son, for later in this life you will journey afar in your role as the torch-bearer. Many of the lands you will visit will also undergo great changes and it is vital that you are made aware of them. Come, join us in a vision of the future." Grasping my hand he led me forward into the mists which swiftly closed about me.

We appeared to wander for some considerable time before the mists cleared. Below us were great mountain ranges and vast desert regions dotted the landscape. "What land is this?" I asked curiously.

"It is that known as Australia," replied the Atlantean Teacher, who hovered near by.

This reply set my thoughts racing, for upon my right leg were two birth marks, one of which had a strong resemblance to the outline of this land. "Oooh," I breathed excitedly, "I have always wished to visit this land. I have family links within it, although I have never met that particular branch of the family."

Wen Shu gazed at my excited features. "You will, my son, one day you will, for this land contains a portion of your destiny. Its shores will always draw you to them." Following this remark we began to change direction and moved towards the southerly coastal regions.

Below us was a large city which lay upon a wide flat plain. As we watched, a sound rent the air, not unlike some great clap of thunder. In moments the buildings below us began to topple like houses of cards. Some collapsed upon the cars below, crushing them and their occupants in an instant. Cries of pain and terror rent the air. I watched transfixed, the emotions of the population rising like a great force around us. Finally I whispered: "What city is this?"

He continued to gaze at the scene for a while before replying. "It is known as Adelaide and stands upon an ancient fault line, but this is only the beginning, for this land must also be cleansed." Noting my dismay, he continued: "However, it has a great part to play in the new Age; it will become a mighty spiritually evolved nation, but before that occurs, much else must happen. Come."

We left the scene of destruction behind us and soon arrived over another great city, dotted with skyscrapers and a bridge which was very familiar. "I know that city!" I shouted excitedly, "it is Sydney; it has the same bridge as my own city of Newcastle."

Gazing benevolently at me, Wen Shu nodded. "You are indeed correct, it is Sydney. However, please observe." Directing my gaze out to sea I soon observed a gigantic wall of water which silently leapt towards the city. With an enormous roar it thundered down upon the glistening buildings, smashing them apart like matchwood. The great Opera House, with its futuristic design, was cast into the air like a giant toy. The waters rushed inland, sweeping away all before them. Grim silence followed their return to the sea, taking with them the debris of a once proud city.

"Oh my God!" I cried. "Why? And how?"

"The answer to 'how' is easier than 'why'," replied the Atlantean. "That particular tidal wave was set in motion due to a sea-bed earthquake in the region of the fire-islands known to you as Fiji. These islands are really the mountain tops of an ancient land, known once as Mu, or Lemuria. That land is also about to rise above the waves and it is that which causes the havoc you have just witnessed. As to why, we can but point to gross materialism. Man must change, either voluntarily or through severe shock. In some cases, only shock will suffice," he added grimly.

"This land will receive attacks on her northern shores also, for the area adjacent to the lands of Indonesia are also extremely volatile and many great waves will thunder down upon the civilizations in that region," he went on.

I gazed at him incredulously. This land of my boyhood dreams was being completely washed away. "Please, I must know, why will this happen, what brings it about?"

The Atlantean, realizing that we could not get any further until my questions were satisfactorily answered, replied: "The 'why' lies deep beneath the surface of the planet. There exist what your scientists term 'plates' beneath the earth's crust and these move upon the molten core of the planet. There are a number of these and the land of Australia sits upon one known as the Pacific Plate. This is the largest of the 'plates' and stretches from the eastern portion of Australia to the Americas, where it meets another 'plate' along the fault line sited in California, of which we have spoken at other times."

Seeing that I was listening attentively he continued: "However, to the north of Australia is located another 'plate', upon which is the Indonesian and Indian continents. This one is extremely volatile and the 'plates' are in continual motion. When they meet, they set up earthquake activity, which in turn sets in motion tidal waves, which traverse the oceans until they are halted by a land mass. Although the South Pacific Plate is relatively stable, it is subject to the effects set in motion by reaction with adjoining 'plates'."

He left a few moments for this to sink in, then said: "Now we must journey to a near-by land which also contains a portion of your destiny."

Reluctantly I followed the Brothers into the mists and soon we were hovering over two large islands.

"Is this New Zealand?" I asked.

"It is indeed, my son," answered Wen Shu, "now watch very carefully."

The seas in the region of these islands began to boil and great jets of water shot high into the air. As we watched, clouds of steam rose from the area of the ocean, within which I could vaguely make out a land mass rising from the bed of the ocean. Giant waves were set in motion by this eruption and these wreaked havoc upon the adjacent islands, some racing off into the distance to crash upon the shores of the Australian continent. It seemed that I watched this scene for hours, although in the Earth time scale it must have been many months. As the disturbances subsided, they left upon the surface a dark steaming mass of rock which in size greatly dwarfed both of its neighbours.

"Observe closely," the Atlantean directed, pointing in the direction of the coastal regions of both lands. Great tidal waves were hurling themselves upon the coastal cities, destroying all in their path. Little escaped, cities were crushed beneath the force of the waves, some of which towered some three hundred feet above the surface of the sea. The people were torn from their homes and tossed like broken dolls upon the waters, their bodies dragged out to sea with each receding wave. Scenes of total destruction lay before my gaze on all sides.

Struck dumb by what I had been made to observe, I could but stare at those who had revealed such horror to me. Answering my unspoken question the Atlantean replied: "It is part of the Plan — a Plan all were aware of when incarnating. The new land which arises was once a part of the old Lemurian continent. Other portions will rise off the coasts of the North and South Americas. Once all necessary changes have been undergone, these three lands — Australia, New Zealand and the New Land — will provide a great point of light, of hope, and of peace for the New Age Man; indeed, eventually, for the new race which will succeed your current race."

"How can you say that?" I cried wildly, unable to contain my emotion any longer. "The people were all wiped out. None could have withstood those waves."

He waited for my fervent emotions to cool, then said, "The wise among them did not perish, for that was also part of the Plan. They were advised to move into the arid heart, where they will survive. Come, let us journey."

Taking my hand in his gently, he led me once more into the mists. Soon the continent of Australia lay beneath us and as we headed north, I noted the great desert regions I had observed earlier. Here a great transformation was taking place. The unbearable heat had been reduced considerably and upon the sands, grass now grew, turning this once arid region into a green haven. Many people were to be seen tending the land, attempting to coax crops from it.

"But it is so different. From where did they obtain the water?" I asked, somewhat puzzled.

"There are mighty lakes deep beneath the surface, and the upheavals in the Earth's crust in divers places has released the previously inaccessible waters. Now Man will sustain himself and his descendants for many centuries. Here you will find the better portions of the Aryan race, from whom will be selected those who will provide the seeds for the new Race of Tan."

J

"Then all is not lost — there is a positive tomorrow?" I asked, half questioningly.

"For those who were prepared to change their outlook, prepared to free themselves of the things of matter, casting aside illusionary power and embracing universal brotherhood — yes, there is hope, my son. Did you really doubt it?" he asked, gazing deeply into my eyes.

I glanced away before replying. "I . . . I am not sure. With all the gloom and doom, I think I did begin to doubt it. Thank you for something positive to build upon," I said, looking towards all the assembled Brothers, without whom none of this would have been possible.

"Good, good, my son, you progress," cried Wen Shu cheerfully. "Now we must return you to your point in time and to your present life." With that the mists closed about us and I was soon back with Aileen relating the incredible happenings of the evening.

Chapter 22

For the next two months there was no further communication from the Brothers and we were left in a state of suspended animation, awaiting further direction and in particular further information on my past experience in the art of healing. When it came, it was not quite what I had expected. The Brothers suddenly rejoined our meditation just prior to the winter solstice, which as it happened, was more than appropriate.

Gazing benevolently at us, Wen Shu bade me prepare myself for further journeyings into the past. "I will today reveal an important link in your past, for it has deep patterns which relate to your future. This was experienced in the female form around 200 B.C. in a Celtic tribe in Britain, as one of seventeen children dwelling on the great plain where the mighty standing stones are to be located even in your present time. It was a hard life, physically, for rising at dawn you would spend most of your day tending the sheep on the wind-swept plain. The evenings were spent in weaving wool for clothing, salting meat for the winter and producing mead from the honey supplied by the bees."

He paused a moment, then smiling at my concentrated interest, continued: "Upon the death of your father, your mother and her six surviving children came under the protection of her brother, your Uncle Cerdic, who was the Druid for the tribe. This soul was important to you in as much as that he was the priest largely responsible for your early demise in the Fire Temple of Atlantis." Once more the mists closed about me and I was back in time.

Uncle Cerdic was a tall, silent man with deep set eyes which appeared to pierce one's very being, and Mother and my brothers and sisters tended to scuttle away whenever he appeared. His role as the Druid lent an air of mystery to him and Mother greatly feared him, encouraging us to follow her lead. Although grateful for his support, she could not treat him as a normal family member because of his link with magical forces. It took quite some time for him to adjust to his new family, having dwelt alone in his isolated cottage on the edge of the plain until the time we joined him.

During the first winter we spent together, Uncle Cerdic began to relate to us the story of how the mighty stones were erected at near-by Stonehenge. As the firelight flickered upon his drawn face, half hidden as it was by a long grey beard, he had an air of a sorcerer about him, and his voice seemed mysterious.

" 'Tis said that the great stones were erected by the priests of a long gone land which lay far out in the mighty ocean. This land was once known as fabled Atlantis, which in its prime ruled the world, so great were its armies. They were a mighty people, giants they were, who towered some ten or twelve feet tall." We all gasped at this, although my mother, busy at her spinning wheel, only gave a wry smile. He continued, noting our obvious enjoyment and rapt attention, "The people lived in houses more like palaces. Glowing white, they were, all with roofs of gold." At this we broke out in excited chatter, for what would we not give for a sturdy roof over our heads in place of the turf which tended to leak badly in a heavy storm.

Uncle Cerdic resumed his tale. "They had a grand temple built high upon a mountain, from which the priests would beam down great rays of light upon the people, controlling them, encouraging them to act in accordance with the Great Law." Our eyes grew large at this thought, gazing around us fearfully to ascertain that Uncle Cerdic was not doing the same. Amused at our reaction he continued: "But the people were warlike and took to fighting among themselves, taking less and less notice of the priests."

"But why, Uncle Cerdic?" I questioned. "If the priests could control them with the rays, why did that happen?"

He gazed at me, pulling his beard thoughtfully. "Well, Brigid, they took to sorcery and the practice of the black arts."

I shivered, suddenly afraid, but was still anxious to know more. "And then?" I whispered tremulously.

"The land itself turned against the people. Great volcanos sprang into life, casting fire and destruction upon the cities and the land heaved and shook, giant crevasses opened in the earth, swallowing many people. The land eventually broke apart into small islands, teaching the people a much needed lesson."

"What happened after that, Uncle?" I queried, eager to learn more.

"For a long time they lived in peace," he answered, "but eventually they took to the black arts once more and even greater Earth shaking took place, many of the islands sinking beneath the sea. The people came to rest eventually upon one part of their former kingdom, which they called Poisedonis and the priests endeavoured to lead them back to the worship of the One God, but once again the people turned away. Eventually they turned to self worship, where they created statues of themselves and placed them in the temples in order that their friends and associates might worship them. At this point in time the remains of the true priesthood began to leave and some of them settled here, where they set up the standing stones."

"But why, Uncle Cerdic, what purpose did they serve?" I asked curiously.

Giving me one of his rare smiles he replied: "They mark the points where the great energies meet within the Earth. At times of Solstice and Equinox, great energies flow into and are drawn out of the Earth from elsewhere in the great beyond. These energies travel along the high points of our land and we find today that great stones are erected upon the tors and hills, to indicate the path of the power which we call Ley. In the time of the Spring Equinox we celebrate the return of the power, for it will bring forth the crops and the land will bloom. At the time of High Summer Solstice we give thanks for the plentitude and for the continuance of the energies, that the harvest might be bountiful at the time of the Autumnal Equinox."

Mother interrupted at this point: "'Tis time the children were abed, Cerdic." So saying she gathered up the youngest, despite the howls of protest at the untimely ending of the story. Uncle Cerdic merely laughed and patted me on the head, then turned to the fire and gazed thoughtfully into it.

The following summer Uncle Cerdic began to take me with him on trips across the plain in search of the herbs he used in his Druidic rites. These he taught me to recognize and to know by name. He also instructed me in the practice of drying the herbs and various roots used in certain potions, for he said he had need of a young assistant. So began a training which would lead me into strange situations. My long hours spent with the flocks encouraged me to dwell in thought upon the many things which Uncle Cerdic told us during the winter nights, and slowly, I became aware of the nature elementals around and about me.

At first I thought I was dreaming, that I had in fact dropped off to sleep. Rubbing my eyes I returned my gaze to the spot, and there was the same small figure, which seemed to be composed of the very earth and yet had a personality of its own. "Are you really there?" I asked incredulously.

He gazed at me consideringly before replying. "Of course I am, why do you doubt it?"

"Well, I have never ever seen the like of you before. What are you?"

He turned away crossly at this question, beginning to trample earth under his feet.

"Oh please do not go away, I did not mean to offend you, but I have never seen the little people before. You are one of them, are you not?" I asked, hoping anxiously that he would return.

Looking sulkily over his shoulder he said: "Of course I am!"

Happy that he had condescended to reply I asked: "What are you doing?"

"Why, making soil of course; what are you doing?" he replied impatiently.

"Oh, I am minding the sheep," I answered readily.

"What for? They are quite capable of looking after themselves," he snorted.

"Oh yes I know, but they may wander off and get lost," I explained.

He shook his head in puzzlement and returned to his work, taking no more notice of me.

Gazing at him forlornly I ventured to ask: "Will you come back again?"

He looked down his nose at me and muttered, "I am always here, it is *you* who will have to return." Whereupon he disappeared into the earth itself.

From that point on I was aware of many of the elementals, who seemed ever busy, having little time to note my presence or the fact that I was observing them. One evening I decided to ask Uncle Cerdic about them, in the hope that he might cast some light upon their habits. His eyes lit up as I told him what I had been observing. "Ah, 'tis 'the gift' you have. I should have recognized it before," he answered, his face a study of joy and perplexity. "But what are we to do with you, for 'the gift' must not be wasted?"

I stared at him, not understanding. "What gift, Uncle Cerdic?"

"Why, the Seeing Eye, Brigid; you are blessed," he said, pleasure in his tone of voice.

"What am I to do with it?" I asked, still puzzled as to his meaning.

"That remains to be seen my child. I must give this some thought. Placing his arm fondly around my shoulders he continued: "I will let you know, but first I must have words with your mother. Now on your way and get on with your duties."

Nothing more was said for some considerable time,

although Mother began to cast fearful glances in my direction from time to time. With the return of winter, Uncle Cerdic began once more to regale us with stories of the Druids.

"Tell us about the time you journeyed to the other land, Uncle Cerdic," we chorused one evening, for we were all aware that in his youth he had been taken across the sea to train for his role as the Druid. Gazing cheerfully at the sea of faces, rather enjoying his role of story-teller, he stirred up the embers of the fire before starting.

"Well now," he began, "it is a very long time ago and I am not at all sure I can remember."

"Oooh, please, please tell us," we begged, grasping his arm pleadingly.

"Now children, leave your Uncle Cerdic be," Mother interrupted.

"Oh, it is no bother, no bother at all, I was only jesting," he replied. "Well then, it was many years ago, when I was but some four and twenty years, that I was taken over the sea to the land they call the Emerald Isle, for there they have great colleges where the Druids train for the brotherhood. It was found that I had 'the gifts', but it was necessary for me to be trained in their use. It was there I was taught to communicate with the Devas of trees and the earth." At this, I gazed at him speculatively, wondering if I was about to be sent to such a college also.

"But that was only the half of it," he continued, "for we were trained in solar worship, to plot the course of the stars in the heavens and — once we had passed the various levels of initiation — to participate in the great festivals. A part of my training was to learn to develop my healing gift and this was very long and laborious, indeed I doubted that I would ever master it." His eyes twinkled, for as they travelled around the faces of his audience, he noted many signs of fear.

"How did they teach you to communicate with the Devas, Uncle Cerdic? Can you teach us?" asked one of my brothers.

Amused, he shook his head. "First you must possess the gift of the Seeing Eye." He cast a speculative look at me, but refrained from comment, although Mother glanced at me fearfully. "But," he went on, noting their disappointment, "it is simple once you know how. The nature forces long to communicate with us, so if you go into the glades, you will find them there, making the soil, tending the growth of the trees and plants. If you will sit quietly and send out a thought of love, they will come and talk to you." The eyes of the younger ones grew large at this, wondering how soon the weather would clear in order that they might try this for themselves.

"What happened when you finished your training, Uncle Cerdic?" I asked, anxious to know what might lie ahead of myself. "Did you come back here to take up your present role?"

Pulling his beard he replied: "No Brigid, I journeyed to many lands, as most of the brotherhood did, in order that I might in turn instruct others."

My eyes widened at the thought of journeying afar. "Where did you go? Please tell us."

Ruminating for a moment or two, he continued: "Well, first I journeyed to the land of the Saxons and for two years I worked in a great forest, healing the sick and training young men with 'the gift' to do the same. Some I taught the art of solar worship and others the gift of prophecy. After that time I was asked to journey to the area of a sea called Mediterranean and for some five years I taught and instructed many who also possessed 'the gifts'. But I grew weary of the journeyings and longed to return to my own land and eventually made my way back here. There are armed forces multiplying in those lands of the Mediterranean, which makes it difficult for those of the faith, for they have different gods and kill many of the brotherhood in their determination to establish their own faith."

"What forces are they?" I asked, wondering if he referred to evil forces.

"I speak of vast armies which are ravaging the lands by the shores of that great sea," he said. "They come from a great city called Rome and seem determined to rule the world. 'Tis to be hoped that they do not reach our shores, for they worship a strange fire god and 'tis said that they offer human sacrifices to it." We all shivered in fear on hearing this, partly due to the tale — and also due to the many tales we had heard of similar rites in the forests held by the Druids.

In the spring Uncle Cerdic called me to follow him in to the forest and soon we entered a glade where several men in long white robes were gathered. Grasping my hand, Uncle Cerdic led me forward and bade me face the assembled Druids. I was deeply fearful, not at all certain what my fate was to be, for Uncle had not given me any indication of what lay ahead. For an hour I was questioned, told to gaze around me and explain what I saw. My mind in a torment, I answered wildly, fearful of what may happen if I did not. Eventually, the questioners withdrew and talked quietly and earnestly amongst themselves. Finally they returned, with Uncle Cerdic as their spokesman.

He came towards me and said: "You did well my child. It is the considered opinion of the brothers that you have 'the gift' and that you should now be initiated into the ranks of the Druids."

I gazed at him fearfully. "What . . . what . . . does that mean? What will happen to me?"

He patted my hand, whilst saying, "No need to fear my child. We will call upon you prior to the time of the High Solstice, when you will be symbolically passed over the fire."

I gasped and withdrew my hand hurriedly. "I'm not sure that I want that." I glanced about me fearfully, wondering if I ought to run.

"There is naught to fear, child, it is a symbolic passing over fire. You will not be placed within it. I will instruct you in the months ahead." He paused a moment, then said: "Now return to your duties with the flocks." I needed no urging, but took to my heels and fled the glade.

During the intervening months as spring lengthened into summer, Uncle Cerdic instructed me on what lay ahead of me during my initiation ceremony. My fears subsided as I realized that my physical form would not come to any harm, that in fact it was the spirit form which would be tested during this coming ceremony. I was to eliminate fear from my mind, for this would have a negative effect upon me if shown or felt during the ceremony. He began to teach me to enter into the stillness of the mind, to still my thoughts and become one with the Great Force of All Light.

The day prior to the great Solstice I was refused all food, needing to free the mind and body to undergo the initiation. Taken away from my family for this period, I spent the day with Uncle in deep silence, entering into the inner stillness where, with the help of the herbs he bade me eat, I began to observe amazing happenings around me. The atmosphere about us became bright and clear, the colours of the trees and surrounding foliage taking on a brilliance I had not observed before. The elementals were all clearly visible, taking little notice of us, just going about their daily tasks. Slowly I drifted from my body and was taken by Uncle, who apparently had awaited my coming, into a different level of consciousness. All was misty at first, but I soon discerned many who appeared to be Druids, for they too were clad in long white robes, but they were quite unlike any of the Druids I had so far encountered. Their skin glowed and they seemed to radiate love towards me, yet I did not know them. Soon we settled down upon a large stone and one by one they began to instruct me.

I returned to consciousness long after the onset of darkness, my body stiff, all circulation having apparently ceased. Uncle Cerdic began to rub my limbs, swiftly bringing back the glow to stiffened muscles. Taking me by the hand he said, "Now my child, you must bathe in the pool in yonder glade and then we will take you to the high place." The thought of bathing in the cold water of the forest pool at this hour did not fill me overmuch with joy, but I did as I was bid, fearing to object at this late stage. Finally I donned the long white robe which Uncle Cerdic had left for me to wear.

His hand firmly holding mine, we set off into the night, although faint glimmers of light on the horizon indicated that dawn was not far off. As we approached the tor, many ghostly figures could be observed flitting through the gathering dawn, like spectres in some childhood tale. As we stumbled up the rocky path, my heart began to beat alarmingly as I tried to subdue my fears. Uncle Cerdic squeezed my hand, as though in answer to my fears, giving me courage to continue.

We entered a large circle of standing stones in the centre of which stood a large flat stone supported by two smaller stones. Upon this was what appeared to be a large pile of brushwood. Swallowing hard, I hung on to Uncle Cerdic's hand as we took our place among the assembled Druids. As the sun began to rise, one figure in a hooded robe entered the circle and made his way to the altar — for such it was. Raising his arms heavenwards he began a loud incantation to the Cosmic

Source of All Light. As his arms stretched upwards, the assembled Druids all began a similar invocation and soon I perceived a small wisp of smoke arising from the pile of brushwood on the altar. As the sun rose higher, the smoke increased until a tongue of flame leapt forth, to exultant cries from the assembled throng.

As the flames took hold, strong hands grasped me from behind and I was lifted on high. Terrified, I tried hard to close my eyes, fearing that my end was at hand. At this point I was handed to the High Druid who slowly passed me over the flames, although far enough away to prevent any harm coming to me. My mind hard at work to still the fear within me, I could not register the strange incantation which was made over me. The flames seemed to leap high about me and the one who supported me, yet none touched us in any way. As the flames died away I was gently lowered to the earth and my brow marked with an unknown substance. Bade to kneel, I was inducted within the order of the Druids and made to take an oath of allegiance and total silence. The rest of that ceremony passed in a haze, so confused was I by all that was happening to me.

The ceremony complete, I was led away by my uncle and returned to my family. Here, to my great sadness, I encountered a withdrawal of affection, for my family, now aware of my new role, feared me and would no longer accept me as they had before. Uncle had forewarned me that this might possibly happen, but I had not believed him. I returned to my solitary duties of watching the flock, with ample time to ponder on the happenings of High Summer Solstice.

From that time on, Uncle sought me out on various occasions and began to teach me the Druidic method of communication. This took the form of twigs, bent into what he told me was known as the Greek Alphabet. If I needed to leave a message, I was to do so in this manner upon the branch of a tree in order that my brother Druids might receive it. He also began to teach me the art of prophecy which he told me I had brought with me from an earlier lifetime, and began to instruct me in the art of healing as well.

So began an intensive period of study which took some years to complete. Interspersed within this training were the High

Festivals, which were undertaken at different points. The majority of the Druidic festivals were held under the giant oaks deep in the forests, far from prying eyes, although some were held, as had been my baptism, upon the tor. At the times of the great Festivals, I accompanied Uncle to fast and to pray within the great standing stones and on such occasions I was often used as a channel for spirit communication, given visions and prophetic utterances.

One festival I loved more than any other — this was the Festival of Light, held at the time of the Autumnal Equinox. This always took place within the great standing stones on the high tor and brought for me a magic which could not be equalled elsewhere. Entering the stones silently, we would stand in a large circle, arms linked, eyes cast heavenwards into the night sky. Into the centre of the circle the High Priest would slowly walk, bearing with him a great flaming torch.

Following deep invocation for light for the planet from the Cosmic Source, all would slowly move to the centre of the circle where each would light a small torch from the large torch held by the High Druid, then returning to our places, we would continue our invocation for light. As this progressed there appeared within the centre of the group a circle of spirit brothers, each holding aloft a flame of an etheric substance which greatly added to the light within the circle. Hovering above all torches were small angelic figures.

As the flames from our torches began to dim, the angelic forces swooped down, taking the spiritual or etheric formation of light from us. On the instant, the flames from these torches leapt high into the air, and about their circumference a gleaming band of golden metal appeared.

Soon, within the flame itself, appeared what seemed to be a ball of glass, quite unlike any I had seen before. It was cut upon its surface and it spun swiftly within the golden band, casting the light of the torch far out into the night. As this happened, the angelic beings flew off with the etheric torches and the light was symbolically taken to all parts of the Earth. With the ending of this ceremony, we all departed from the tor, taking with us the flickering remnants of our torches. From afar, as I gazed back, it created a scene of almost magical beauty to my eyes, although no doubt to the fearful populace it was a sight they would much rather not look upon, fearing what they did not understand.

The vision began to fade and all too soon I found myself back within the circle of the Brothers, with Wen Shu gazing seriously at me. I waited for him to relate the ending of that life experience.

He began: "None was long-lived in those days of wattle and daub huts; largely due to the poor diet, you succumbed to the 'coughing disease' in your mid-twenties. Your uncle was visiting his colleagues in Ireland at that time and your family nursed you in a half-hearted manner, which subsequently led to your death. It was a short life, but very illuminating, indicating once again the path of prophecy and healing undertaken in difficult conditions. Many of the brother Druids you encountered in that lifetime were priestly links with your days in Atlantis and they completed the Karmic Cycle through Druidic service.

Wen Shu paused a moment to let this sink in, then continued: "Once again you should be able to see the pattern evolving. Through many hard lives you have followed the inner path, taking initiation after initiation, all in preparation for the period which awaits you later in your current life cycle."

I gazed at him questioningly at this comment. "Surely it could not have been known what I was to undertake so far in advance?"

He smiled at me. "My son, you forget that there is no such thing as chance. All takes place according to Cosmic Law. All was foreseen and planned well in advance. Forget your concept of time, realize that all is now, and that what has happened to you is but a mere instant in the great Cosmic pattern. Now we must leave, for this has been a long and taxing experience for you." With that, he and the Brothers simply vanished from view.

Chapter 23

The following weeks were spent in discussing with Aileen the results of the most recent journey into my past and tying up the loose ends. We were both agreed that much of that revealed was reflected in characteristic traits which were part of my current personality, serving to confirm much that the Brothers had revealed at other times. The gifts of prophecy, visionary capacities and healing talent were obvious in all of the major lives reviewed, but how to couple these with the horrific schedule ahead of the planet? It seemed to me to be quite insurmountable, despite the assurances of the Brothers. Obviously further information on the future was necessary, in order that I might obtain a clearer picture of that which I was to fulfil.

Almost as though they were waiting for this decision, the Brothers reappeared, with Wen Shu at their head, causing Aileen to laugh uproariously.

"We understand the reason for your mirth, but surely by now you have both become accustomed to our sudden appearances and the reasons for them?" smiled Wen Shu.

Aileen nodded her head in agreement, but was still unable to control her amusement.

As she subsided into silence, Wen Shu continued: "You wish further information upon the future of Man, is that not so, my son?" He raised his eyebrows at me questioningly.

"Yes, yes, we do," I exclaimed, "so much about the past fits together, but I am still uncertain as to the future. A great deal of the stress appears to be located in the United States of America. Why is that?"

At this question, the Atlantean spoke. "This is largely due to the role it must play in the Age yet to come. It must give rise to a new race, a new way of life."

I pondered this reply for awhile. "Does this refer only to the United States? I had gathered the impression that other continents would also support the new race."

He half smiled at my comment. "You are indeed correct in your assumption, for there are other lands into which the new race will be born. After the United States, there comes the continent of Australia, also that of France and India, and to a degree, England also. However, before those continents and nations may see the birth of the new and the strong, they must first feel the insurgence of Darkness."

I waited quietly, knowing that he would continue. "All that Man has built up of a materialistic nature in those lands will be torn down. They will come under attack from the insidious doctrines which exclude God from human concepts, but look not to Russia for this. All of these lands will undergo great turmoil and eventual cleansing."

Feeling it right to interrupt at this point, I asked: "By cleansing, do you mean earthquakes and tidal waves?"

"In part, my son, in part," he replied. "Perhaps it is time to take you forward into the final decade of this your current century and reveal to you that which will occur in a geophysical manner to the planet."

My heart sank at these words, for I had hoped that I had seen all that was to occur on that level. Nodding my head in glum agreement, I sat and entered into the meditative silence, within which the Brothers would take me travelling into the future. Soon the mists took over once more and we travelled at great speed to a point, which when the mists cleared, revealed a scene of stark horror. Below us the Earth was being rent apart as the surface collapsed under the weight of gigantic waves crashing upon the shores. The land itself began to heave visibly and the sea rushed inland at an amazing speed. Land which only moments before had been seen to be fruitful, supporting life, suddenly vanished beneath great waves. It was as though the land gave up the struggle against the onrush of the sea and collapsed. Far and wide the waves spread, causing havoc and terror among the populace.

"Where are we?" I asked eventually.

"This is the land you know as the United States of America. Watch carefully," came the reply. For what seemed an age in itself, we watched the great waves rolling inland, mighty cities collapsing under the stress.

"Now you may see the outcome, my son," Wen Shu said softly in my ear. "Large portions of the States of Washington, Idaho, Montana, Wyoming, Kansas, Nebraska, Oklahoma, Texas, and Arizona are affected now by the waters; but they will survive. Not so those lands which now lie beneath the waters."

"Which are they?" I whispered.

"The majority of the State of California, although you can see that large portions have now become offshore islands. Also the majority of Oregon, Utah and Colorado have gone for ever. To compensate, there are new lands rising. Look — out into the Pacific Ocean."

Casting my gaze in the direction indicated, I could indeed see new land appearing from beneath the boiling waters. An elongated strip of land some hundred or so miles in length was now visible, although it was dark and forbidding, appearing to be of a volcanic construction. Gazing inland I saw once great coastal cities now marooned offshore — all that was left of the vast state of California.

"Let us look at the cities on the eastern seaboard now," said the Atlantean, taking me once more into the mists. As we emerged, similar scenes were being enacted below us. The remnants of New York were being battered considerably by the force of the on-shore waves. The near-by State of New Jersey was totally inundated as were the Atlantic cities of Pittsburgh and Boston.

"But why?" I asked pleadingly, seeking for some sense to be brought into this vision.

The Atlantean replied quietly, "These cities have ancient Atlantean Karmic energies. Many within them have reacted in a negative manner to the influx of new Age ideals. In this they have provided a testing ground for other egos incarnated there. Now it is time for the cleansing. Later, new life will flow into these points, bringing back vitality to the land." He waited a minute while I digested this, then said urgently, "We have not yet completed the scene; come with us."

Once more we entered into the mists. Soon we were hovering over the area of the Great Lakes, covering the States of Wisconsin, Michigan and Illinois. Enormous havoc had been sustained here and the lakes had greatly increased in size, virtually drowning the great industrial cities built upon their shores. The Atlantean spoke quietly: "These waters will now change their direction and will begin to empty into the Gulf of Mexico."

I gazed dumbly at the scene. "There is not a great deal left, is there? Was it necessary for one continent to take such great blows?"

He nodded as he spoke: "Yes indeed, for ancient Karmic patterns are being worked out. This land will one day become the land of the free. Free in the true sense of the word. One day, the Light for the new Age will walk this land; it must become purified before that day dawns."

Still unable to comprehend, I continued: "But I have always thought of this as a great nation; it supports a major portion of the world, opens its doors to the races, offers great opportunities for Man."

His smile was gentle as he answered: "Indeed my son, you are correct. Great souls from long ago Lemuria have entered into life experience within this land and sought to influence the many who would follow the more destructive Atlantean egos incarnate here. The latter have led the nation far, founded its wealth and hence its strength in world matters, but this has now gone too far. Now there must be an elimination of the gross, the ugly, and the dark energies which have permeated the land. It was once pure, raised from the bed of the ocean specifically to provide a new opportunity for the more evolved Atlantean egos."

Realizing that I was still deeply confused, Wen Shu intervened. "My son, for more than a century the nations of your planet have become more and more involved in self interest. It has become the rallying call of those in world government and also within the great religions. Interest in, and consideration for others, is more and more being set aside, self interest abounds. There is a growing disharmony world wide, which in itself sows the seeds of great discord. The race of Man is speedily heading towards Self-Awareness, vital to outgrowth for the coming Age. However, Mankind is responding to the lower vibration of this call, ignoring the true self — the reality within — and is concentrating more and more upon the lower, illusionary self, becoming self-indulgent at the expense of his brother Man. Hence the need for great cleansing on the level you have witnessed."

A glimmer of light was appearing within my mind, but all was still not clear. "When you say 'self-awareness' do you mean

K

that the race of Man over all is meant to become aware of his spiritual self as the true self?"

He beamed at me. "Yes my son, I do. The note of 'self-awareness' has been sounded within the ethers, but many have translated this as a need to concentrate upon the physical self, for they relate to the lower ego alone. So few comprehend the fact that they are more then physical form. The great religions have assisted in this in seeking to maintain their power over sections of the community. You therefore have the situation upon your planet whereby many starve, compelled to live in abject squalor, due to the self-interest of his brothers elsewhere upon the globe."

Although I was now beginning to understand in part, I still could not see how this could be translated to the ordinary man or woman in the street. "Many will still ask 'why'. What do I tell them?"

The Atlantean spoke first. "It is necessary for all to be aware that every nation has a blueprint for lives undertaken within it. A Cosmic Force creates the patterns and subsequently encourages the development of all who incarnate in that nation. The gift of the Creator is free will, and to a degree all who incarnate are encouraged to follow the National blueprint within the framework of their free will. However, there are those who bring with them from ancient Atlantean times, memories of past greatness, and these obtain positions of power. They lead the race along illusionary paths, offering materialistic wealth and power to those who follow. Before long the nation is headed towards self-destruction and the need for drastic intervention is necessary. Mankind can prevent all that has been and will be revealed to you, if he will begin to return to his original patterns, embrace brotherhood and share that which he has with those who have not."

I gazed at him in awe. "It all sounds so simple; why then has it not been attempted?"

He merely looked at me, allowing me to draw my own conclusions, then spoke again: "We have not as yet concluded our journey into the future. Other nations will be undergoing great change at this point in time. Come, let us proceed." With this, we entered into the mists once again.

As we swooped down upon the globe, he indicated lands

which were undergoing great upheavals. The sounds of destruction filled the air, together with cries of terror, as nation after nation was struck. I gazed at him questioningly.

"These are the lands which are dominated by Islamic law. You will have cause to remember the might of Islam before this century draws to its close. Look below you; affected are the lands of Syria, Iran, Iraq, Turkey, and also Israel, caught in their midst."

Soon we were hovering over the Mediterranean Sea, but greatly changed, for it was now blocked, land having appeared between Spain and Africa.

"Yes my son," said Wen Shu softly, "the ancient land bridge has reappeared, leaving the way open for onslaughts of a different kind."

"Come," the Atlantean commanded, and we set off once more. This time a vast continent lay below us. "China," was his terse comment. As we hovered around the great cities, much devastation was evident. Around the city of Peking vast areas were now flooded, forming gigantic lakes, large sections of the ancient wall having vanished. The people were huddled together against the force of the great winds, abject in their loss. "This," said the Atlantean, "will set in motion a great exodus, which will lead these people to overrun many other nations in search of food."

Swiftly we passed over the scenes of devastation. Russia appeared to be reeling under the effect of mighty earthquakes in many of her cities. Large portions of her coastline were being pounded by great waves, extensive tracts of land disappearing beneath the waves. In Europe, much of Finland, Sweden, Norway, Denmark and England was under water; Ireland and Scotland too. With the upheavals, earlier predictions by the Brothers were seen to be coming true. The west coast of England was now jutting high above the seas, but what had been great east coast ports were barely visible now, hidden deep beneath the waves. It was as though a giant hand had up-ended the British Isles in an instant, transforming her into a series of mountainous peaks on the west coast, whilst the sea hungrily ate away the eastern shorelines.

Noting my great distress at the scenes before me, Wen Shu took my arm and we returned once more into the mists. Soon we were back with Aileen, who patiently awaited my return to consciousness and the telling of what had transpired. The Brothers left silently and I sat for some considerable time, absorbing what I had seen, quite unable to speak. When I did finally recover myself, Aileen and I sat until long into the night discussing the portent of that which had been revealed this time.

Chapter 24

For some months following these revelations I maintained an inner silence, trying vainly to absorb the enormity of what lay ahead of Man. I continually clung to the words of the Atlantean Teacher, that none of it need occur in the manner indicated if Mankind could but turn around. How? I spent many evenings trying to resolve that conundrum. Obviously I had to change myself, in outlook and expression. Again, obviously, that was the whole purpose in showing such scenes to me. However, it was one thing to be aware of the need to change oneself — quite another to accomplish it.

I contemplated the predicted happenings and tried very hard to be dispassionate, looking at the whole situation without emotion. Whenever I came to the point where my own country was involved, particularly my genetic family, I found this exceedingly difficult to maintain. I really needed something positive to focus my thought patterns upon. Mentioning this one evening to Aileen, she replied, "I have been thinking along similar lines. All the indications are that it is thought which is creating the imbalance, therefore we ought to commence with thought."

I gazed at her speculatively. "What exactly do you suggest we do?" I enquired.

She sat in deep thought for a while before replying: "There are two avenues open to us: one is to bring our own thought patterns under complete control, and the other is to attempt to project a ray of light into the etheric envelope which encircles the planet. In a sense, attempting to heal the Earth."

I was startled by her words. "But . . . that is what Wen Shu told me many years ago — heal the Earth . . . ."

She looked at me quizzically. "Then why not do it?"

I looked at her somewhat shamefaced. "I . . . I did for a time . . . but . . . eventually I gave up."

She sighed in exasperation. "Will you never learn? You are given the most amazing help — the form of help I myself have longed for over many years — and you ignore it!"

I shrugged my shoulders, unable to explain to her that so much came from Wen Shu that I had never been quite sure as to how to deal with much of it. Wishing to change the subject, I asked swiftly: "How do you suggest that we bring our thought patterns under control?"

Giving me a long cool look she replied: "Through examining our thoughts at the end of each day, to ascertain where we have created disharmony. The occasions we lose our temper . . . ." She looked warningly at me at this point, then continued, "The many times when we think in a destructive manner when a person or a situation does not co-operate in the manner we expected. Any situation where our thoughts have veered from the positive to the negative."

"And how do we deal with them, once we have located them?" I asked, sensing the answer in advance.

"By projecting a positive thought of love and light towards the person or situation of course!" she exclaimed, feeling that I should not have needed to ask that question.

"Let us commence right away," I said quickly, wishing to direct her displeasure away from me.

"Why not," she replied, "we can try to create the image of the planet in our mind's eye and then focus a ray of pure white light from the Brow Chakra' into the etheric envelope of the Earth."

Seating myself comfortably I did as she suggested, but discovered it to be a much more difficult task than I had imagined. Try as I may, I could not picture the globe of the planet in my mind's eye, but as I began consciously to project a beam of light from my third eye, I was astonished to find that the image of the globe gradually appeared upon my 'inner screen'. With grim determination I focused the beam into the energy field around the planet until finally it became a bright, shining outer field.

Returning to consciousness, I explained to Aileen the difficulty I had experienced at first. Smiling at me she said: "Do not worry overmuch if you are unable to vision the planet or the light. Whatever you think, you create. If your thoughts are upon 'light encircling the planet' then that is what you are setting in motion. It does, I feel, help to intensify the energy if you are able to vision it, but it is not essential."

"Should we do this at a certain time of the day?" I asked excitedly, wishing to continue with this positive form of assistance for the planet.

"No, I do not think it is absolutely vital at this point in time. If we do eventually attract a large number of people to participate in our endeavour, then I think it would be of value. Of course, that is how England was saved during the last war."

Startled, I gazed at her questioningly. "Whatever do you mean?"

"Have you not heard of the Silent Minute?" she asked, and when I shook my head, mystified, she explained. "Well, through the determined efforts of one man, the people were encouraged to link in silent thought for one minute at 9 p.m. every evening. Many felt that this prevented Germany landing her forces upon our shores."

"Then you feel that if we can manage to attract enough people and encourage them to focus light around the planet daily, we can help to offset much of the destruction predicted?" I asked eagerly.

Aileen nodded in reply, waiting to see what else I had to say.

"Then let us start today; there are a lot of people I can suggest this to." I was suddenly excited at the prospect, but she merely smiled at my sudden burst of enthusiasm, no doubt aware of the frailty of many who would soon lose interest in this exercise, as I myself had. Man tended to act only when disaster struck, by which time it was usually too late.

At this point Wen Shu decided to join our discussion. He appeared before us, smiling in a pleased manner. "I am happy that you have both decided to take some positive action in the field of constructive thought." I hung my head in shame, remembering that he had so instructed me a long time ago. "It is not too late, my son, as long as you maintain the exercise and redouble your efforts in bringing this awareness to others. All is not yet lost," he said.

As always, with the immense love he brought to any situation, he managed to make me respond positively. "I am sorry, Wen Shu — I simply had not grasped the full portent of the instruction. Now I will carry it out."

Placing his arm around me he answered: "The full extent of the power of thought is something not realized by the majority of Mankind." Seating himself comfortably he continued: "The majority of the problems which face the races, the suffering which is inflicted by greedy opportunists, all could be eliminated if Man could be taught the power of thought. Indeed, if many of those who are responsible for the greatest suffering could but see how closely their thought patterns are monitored, they would turn aside. Instead, they grow rich and powerful, many of them turning to religion in later years, hoping to find some form of salvation and expiation in prayer and financial donations. This, my son, is why it is vital that you attend to your studies, and that you fully grasp the nettle of thought control. It is one of your many tasks this time around."

Gazing at him dolefully I answered: "In other words, I am still battling with my failure in Atlantis as Mneb-Ra." When, I wondered, would I ever erase those Karmic patterns?

Smiling compassionately at me, Wen Shu replied: "In part, my son, but you have taken giant strides since that lifetime. The Karmic energies created in that life have long since been erased from the Akasha."

I looked at him in startled disbelief. "But . . . I thought . . . I thought I was here this time to make recompense for that lifetime."

"In that you are mistaken my son. In revealing the life as Mneb-Ra we endeavoured to forewarn of the dangers which accompany power. In addition, we sought to illustrate the need to complete many of the tasks commenced in that far-gone time. In particular, there is the overwhelming need to instruct others in the control of thought patterns," here he paused, then added quietly, "having duly mastered this lesson yourself, of course."

The relief which flooded my being at his comments was immense; it was as though a great weight had been lifted from my shoulders. Ever since being made aware of the Mneb-Ra experience I had been weighed down with a sense of guilt. The knowledge that I had in fact repaid my debt in this direction, helped me to view my future with greater enthusiasm.

Smiling at my reaction, Wen Shu continued: "Along with many members of your Group Soul, you consciously chose to return at this point in time. All answered the call of the Creator which permeated the ethers, reaching into every level of awareness. You follow Cosmic Patterns this time my son, although you must also in some measure meet your past face to face within certain situations. Despite this, it is a planetary purpose which you serve, and your labours must be within the field of service to your brother Man in his hour of need."

"Can you explain this to me, Wen Shu?" I asked humbly.

Gazing cheerfully at Aileen, who sat quietly in her chair observing and noting the interchange, he continued: "But of course, that is the purpose of our meetings, after all. The planet is shortly to commence a new Cosmic Year. This is vastly different to your Earthly year, for it takes some 25,920 terrestrial years to complete. With the dawning of this new Year, great changes will take place upon the planet Earth. The greatest of these will be of a vibratory nature, as every kingdom upon and within the plane of matter undergoes an upward shift in its level of consciousness. This will commence within the mineral kingdom, and you, my son, will have to assist in part of this change."

Rather amazed at this comment, all I could say was, "How?"

He explained: "Long ago, during the Atlantean experiences, you worked with gemstones, utilizing them to aid the return to full health of those given into your care. During your current experience you are to reawaken that awareness and once again utilize the power of the mineral kingdom to aid the return to health of Man. You must instruct others in their use, thus aiding the shift of consciousness within that kingdom."

This I found rather startling, for I had no conscious knowledge on the use of gemstones in the healing act, so I enquired: "May I ask for more information on that please, Wen Shu, for none has ever been given to me?"

Nodding assent he proceeded: "Adjoining the great healing temple in Atlantis, during the early Toltec period, lay a vast cavern within which were to be found gigantic stalactites, far larger than any known today. These were of amethyst and rose quartz in construction, and as pure as spring water. The amethyst variety ranged from a gentle pink to deep violet, whilst the quartz ranged from primrose yellow to deep rose. By means of a passage hewn in the living rock, patients were led into the cavern by the initiate priests, who in turn directed the sick to the particular crystal which would have a beneficial effect upon them. At this stage the priests would 'tune-in' the crystals to the patient, utilizing the still molten core of the planet to achieve this. As you are aware, the lower kingdoms obeyed Man at that point in time, although only initiate priests could bring about the 'tuning-in' process.

"During your period in the Fire Temple, many of these crystals had been incorporated into the healing temples throughout the land and were used to focus the energies upon the sick within the healing wards. They were not as potent in this form, but still emitted powerful healing energies. Prior to the final destruction of Atlantis, these crystals were transported to many lands; Egypt, China and the South Americas. Fragments of those crystals still exist, and provided that you fulfil your appointed role within this lifetime, you, my son, shall be awarded one."

I gasped at this thought, and was deeply intrigued by the knowledge thus imparted. "I find this fascinating, Wen Shu, but why is greater use of the gemstones something which lies upon the horizon? Why has the knowledge faded? Why?"

He held up his hand, smiling broadly. "I seem to have set in motion a veritable torrent of questions! One at a time, please, my son."

My eyes pleading, I nevertheless swallowed the many questions which bubbled up in my mind and awaited his answers.

"The greater use of crystals will occur as Man himself begins to reassemble ancient talents. Many will reincarnate, bearing with them memories of past lives in which they utilized great energies. Not all will be of benefit to the race of Man, of course." He looked rather grim at this point. "However, with them will come those who were priests in the ancient temples, who will reawaken their past awareness and instruct others in the use of the gemstones. During your journeys you will meet such a soul."

"Where? When?" I exclaimed excitedly.

He smiled benevolently at me. "When the time is right, my son, and not before. Simply be aware that there will come a time when you too must begin to utilize ancient skills as you ply your healing craft."

"But I still do not understand why the knowledge has faded, why it is not in use today," I cried in frustration.

Realizing the need for further explanation, Wen Shu continued: "The use of the gemstones faded with the advancement of Man's scientific knowledge, but prior to that it was swept aside as Christianity began to dominate the western hemisphere. For many centuries Man wore gemstones as amulets to ward off the evil eye — all manner of superstitions. The great majority of those amulets were engraved with the symbols of ancient beliefs and handed down from generation to generation. The authorities of the new belief sought to eliminate the past by declaring them to be nothing more than pagan symbols and forbade their continued use. Since that time the greater knowledge of the power locked within the mineral kingdom has disappeared from Man's consciousness."

"You have referred to gemstones and to crystals. Is there a difference?" I asked, intrigued.

"Indeed there is," he answered, "crystals are the rough quartz which contain the vital energies and these are often far more powerful as a healing agent. If obtained whole, still within their rock base, they are living life forms, the younger brothers of creation. They respond like a fine instrument to music and to love, for they are all part of the creative pattern. They emit very powerful energy fields as you will one day discover."

"What of gemstones, how powerful are they?" I questioned.

"Much depends upon their handling at the cutting and polishing stage," he said. "If the one to whom they have been entrusted is envious, if he desires the stone for himself, or if that individual is involved in the black arts, then that stone will absorb these negative energies and bring what Man terms 'bad luck' to whomsoever wears it. There are many great diamonds and rubies upon your planet, which contain undesirable forces set in motion by those who sought to obtain them in the past. You must learn to attune to a gemstone or a crystal, to ensure that it is in harmony with you my son, for not all stones will be."

"How will I learn to achieve that?" I asked, at a loss.

Smiling wisely he replied, "In time you will be so instructed, my son."

This subject was so enthralling that I could not leave it. "Tell me please, which are the most potent of the gemstones?"

Realizing full well my reason for asking, Wen Shu answered: "Within the healing field, the most potent energies are emitted by the pure white crystal quartz. These are located at certain points within your planet Earth, but the purest source lies within a point in the United States of America, known as Arkansas. This has deep links with Lemuria and crystals mined in that region will provide great healing energies. Also within the North Americas can be located many amethyst crystals which, in a sense, are the true healing stones, for they contain a great power. These stones are symbolic of the great initiations and are awarded accordingly. You must not seek to purchase them my son," he added warningly, "for to do so would only bring discontent, as the stone would not be that which is attuned to you."

"How then would I obtain one?" I asked, feeling somewhat frustrated.

He looked at me seriously for a moment, then answered: "As I have stated, they will be awarded to you. When you have undertaken the many tests and trials which await you upon your path of inner awareness, there will appear souls who will give these to you. For whatever reason, they will be motivated to do so, acting as the instruments of the will of the Cosmic Light.

"You must remember my son," he continued gently, "that the amethyst was the stone which signified the Twin-Souls in Atlantis, the evolved beings who incarnated to aid the progress of Man. Much later in the evolutionary pattern they were accorded as a sign of the initiate, worn with pride to signify the ability of that soul to cast aside the pull of matter. When you have so achieved within your current lifetime, as you begin to respond to the energies of the ray of the new Age consciousness, you will be presented with a fragment of one of the ancient Atlantean crystals. Treasure it well, for it has age-old forces of great potency locked within it."

I was somewhat stunned by his comments, but still eager to know more, and asked: "Just what do you mean when you refer to the 'ray of the new Age consciousness'?"

Delighted that his talk was producing so much interest, he answered: "Each new Age comes under different energies, it brings new forces, each with the aim of raising the consciousness of the race of Man. The Age you are entering, the new golden Age of Aquarius, will be an Age dominated by mental energies and the need to utilize them wisely. Man will come under the strong influence of the planet Uranus, the Planet of the Will. The rays of the new race consciousness are those of Indigo and Violet, rays which encourage the race of Man to lift thought patterns beyond the mundane, to concentrate instead upon that which appertains to the spirit self. To this end, those who are responsible for what you term 'fashion' upon the plane of matter, are being influenced to encourage the greater use of these colours. Therefore, in subtle ways, Man is being turned around, for the colours he wears upon his person and with which he decorates his home affect his outlook. Nothing is ever left to chance, my son."

For a moment there was silence as Wen Shu finished speaking, then he said with a gentle smile: "Now I feel I must take my leave, for it has been a long evening for you." With this comment, he faded from view.

Chapter 25

Within two days Wen Shu indicated to me that I was to prepare myself for a further journey into my past. Seeking out my teacher, we both sat in deep meditation awaiting the arrival of my spirit mentor. We sat for some thirty minutes before the atmosphere around us began to change, becoming more intense and charged with a loving energy. As I slowly opend my eyes, the warmly affectionate gaze of Wen Shu met mine. I smiled back at him, speech being totally unnecessary in this interchange of loving greetings.

"As I have earlier indicated, my son," he began, "we must again journey into your past, in order that you might regain awareness of those experiences wherein you pursued your interest in the healing arts. Please be comfortable and I will relate as we enter the state of attunement." Placing his hands upon my head, he continued to talk quietly as the darkness enveloped me.

"This was a life spent in the male body in that land you know as Tibet. It was a peaceful life, a calm period before the storm, one might say. A life of spiritual refreshment, of service, wherein there was no opposition. As a small boy you were given into monastic life by your parents, poor peasants who were quite unable to support their brood and they sought to gain some spiritual reflection from this act, for they hoped, as all families did, that you would one day become an important Llama . . . ."

The building in which I found myself was large, dark and draughty. I gazed about me, partly in fear and partly in curiosity. Never before had I seen such a place. The ceilings and its supports were covered in the most wondrous illustrations of the Lord Buddha, the whole place rang with strange sounds and many people were silently and swiftly moving about. My idyll was interrupted by an impatient shout: "Come along Tchen, no time for dreaming. Come, you are required by Llama Tsien, we must not keep him waiting." I gazed at a boy of some twelve years of age who was gesticulating at me from the doorway. Stumbling to my feet I trotted off after him, totally confused by my new surroundings.

Although it had been explained to me what was happening, I had not yet grasped why my family had placed me within the monastry, and I still hoped that they would soon reclaim me. On entering the Llama's room, my hopes were dashed, for my father was not with him. Gazing at my crestfallen face the Llama smiled and bade me sit upon the floor before him. He studied me for some considerable time before he spoke.

"Well Tchen, how are you adjusting to your new life?" I hung my head, unable to hold back the flood of tears. "Now, now, this will not do. You must learn to adjust, for this will be your home from now on." I stared at him through my tears, observing that his face was kindly and his eyes full of compassion. "You are to come under my charge from now on; I will instruct you and you will sleep here in my room. When I ask you to run errands, you must be swift, but silent in the accomplishment. Do you understand?"

I nodded my head dumbly, thankful that at least he was kind and not as some of the monks I had encountered so far.

Seeing that I was at last receptive, he continued: "Good. Now I want you to familiarize yourself with the Llamasery. Go and explore and return here after you have partaken of the evening meal." He patted me on the shoulder kindly. "Now be on your way." I scuttled off, happy to be free to explore, and to be alone for a time with my thoughts. So began a life which brought to me much contentment and a great deal of spiritual awareness.

As the years passed I grew extremely close to the Llama, for he taught me the ways of my new life. Whereas many of the boys were taught the scriptures and folk tales in parrot fashion, I was instructed with love, the Llama having the ability to bring the ancient tales to life. He patiently related all that was vital to a novitiate monk, helping me to understand and assimilate the deeper meanings behind the tales. It was a spartan life, commencing before dawn with hours of prayer in the temple — harsh discipline for a boy of eight years to accept. Whilst the majority of the novitiates gathered in groups for instruction, I underwent mine in the Llama's private room, something which aroused great resentment in some, who took whatever opportunity they could to humiliate or beat me.

In my fourteenth year, Llama Tsien advised me that it was necessary for me to undergo a minor operation for the opening of my third eye, in order that I might see clearly the higher dimensions. Greatly apprehensive, I followed him to a portion of the Llamasery I had not before entered. He took me into a small room and bade me lie upon the long table; as soon as I was settled a healing Llama commenced drilling in the centre of my brow with a very delicate drill. The pain was excruciating as the drill bit deeper and deeper. Once the task was completed, I was bidden to remain in the room in total darkness until instructed to leave.

Alone in the darkness I was aware of flashing coloured patterns all about me and the most intense pain in the centre of my head. Food was brought to me from time to time and for four days I sat, becoming accustomed to the new dimension as the pains in my head began to subside. From that point on, my training changed, with the Llama Tsien instructing me in the meaning of the colours I was now able to perceive around everyone I encountered. This greatly disturbed me at first, leading for a time to total disorientation.

"What you now see Tchen, is the auric patterns of the brothers," Llama Tsien informed me.

"Yes, but why are they so different?" I asked in awe. "Brother Tsung had great flames of fire leaping from him this morning when I bumped into him on my way here."

He smiled at my wonderment. "That was due to the emotion of anger. Possibly the brother had many difficulties and your clumsiness added to his burden. You must try to walk slowly, you must not run!" Smiling at me gently he continued: "From now on you will be able to see the thoughts of all the brothers reflected in colours within their auras. Likewise, many of them may perceive your thoughts also. This therefore serves as a vital lesson on the need for thought control."

Seeing the wisdom in his words I nodded in agreement, although I wondered how I was going to control my thoughts in the future.

On reaching my eighteenth year I was advised that I was soon to begin the great initiations. My heart filled with great joy on hearing this, for it meant that I had been selected to undergo intensive training in order that I might become a Llama. Sadly it meant that I was now to be separated from my beloved Llama Tsien, who had more than taken the place of my father in my young life. Gazing fondly at me he said softly: "Ahead of you, Tchen, lie difficult years, for you are to be initiated into the occult mysteries, within which you will have to experience both the right hand path and its opposite

— the left hand path. This is vital to teach you the need to follow the middle path of Cosmic One-ness."

Somewhat stunned at his comment, I asked: "Do you mean that I must follow the path of darkness in order to achieve such a goal?"

He nodded gravely at me. "In a manner of speaking, Tchen, it is vital. How can you combat evil if you possess no knowledge of it?"

"But I have no wish to embrace darkness, my only desire is to be as you," I said gazing at him fearfully.

Smiling, he replied: "Then you must first understand the baser aspect of your nature, Tchen. Darkness is but the negative side of the force of light. You have to learn how to ignore its call; to bring the self under total control. However, be warned, the path of magic, be it of light or darkness, has many pitfalls upon it, for power brings with it a great many temptations which are often difficult to resist. This is the reason why you must seek the middle way."

Sadly, I took my leave of him, and approached my new challenge with a heavy heart.

The years which followed were filled with hours of intense study, wherein, for the first time, I came into full realization of the power of my thought, the need to maintain a disciplined thought pattern at all times being constantly hammered home. My study periods were shared with many other novitiates, all of whom responded in a different manner to the tests placed before us. Of these, two young monks became my especial friends over the years, a bond existing between us which felt as though it had links beyond time itself. Indeed, it appeared to me that the brothers Tsung-Li and Lien-Su had always been a part of my life, and this aided us, for we were then able to sustain each other during the long days of testing.

The years passed swiftly and together we underetook initiation upon initiation, but once beyond the fifth level of initiation it became evident that Lien-Su was experiencing great difficulty in maintaining the middle way to Cosmic One-ness. Indeed, with his immensely strong will-power, he turned more and more towards the path of power. He was, of course, under great test, his auric patterns revealing dark energies which had once more become activated by his current studies. Hour after hour I lovingly endeavoured to bring him to redirect his thought patterns, whilst illustrating the danger which lay ahead upon the path he now trod. In this labour of love I was wholeheartedly joined by Tsung-Li, who, although not possessing the strength of character of our beloved brother, did have the ability to throw off unwanted impulses originating within the lower self.

Although not aware of it, we were all under close scrutiny by the Master Initiate, who was aware not only of the current situation, but also of our past links. There was the need for joint action, for if one were to fail, then surely all three would fail. It took more than a year to wean Lien-Su from the darker aspect of his nature and his final accomplishment in mastering his initiation was a great joy to each one of us.

All initiations behind me, I was soon summoned to the sanctum of the High Llama to discuss my future pathway. I gazed inquisitively around this holy of holies, curious to know how the great one lived. He sat upon an enormous cushion in the middle of the floor and his face was grave as he gestured to me to sit, saying, "Be seated, Brother Tchen, we have much to discuss."

I sank to the floor, somewhat apprehensive, not knowing what lay ahead. He put his head on one side and considered me for a moment, then said: "I have consulted your Akashic Record, which indicated that at one point in your past you failed to complete your training in the field of healing and medicine." He spoke in a deep sonorous tone, which had the effect of intensifying the words he uttered. "This must be rectified and as you have completed your initiatory pattern successfully, I wish you to commence training within the School of Medicine." His features were impassive, totally without emotion. "This training will embrace some ten years and you will be taught the art of diagnosis and also that of healing. Go now my son, your future is bright." As he dismissed me his eyes shone with pleasure, producing a warm glow within myself.

The following years were arduous, bringing as they did, many opportunities to unlock the hidden talents of the self. One specific part of this training taught me that it was equally vital for the healer to concern himself with the dying as with

L

the living. Indeed, the later years of my training were spent in long hours coaxing reluctant entities to depart the Earth plane. Often, following long illnesses, these were as bruised and battered as their now discarded physical shell, and they were often full of fear. My task lay in encouraging them to pass on to the higher realms, wherein they would locate the greater reality.

My training finally completed, I opted to remain within the medical school as an instructor, hoping in some small way to repay the great satisfaction I had achieved within its walls. Many happy years followed, during which I gradually accepted greater responsibilities, leading to the time when I became the senior instructor, a role I held for some years before finally fulfilling the dream of my now long deceased parents — that of becoming the High Llama — some years prior to my death.

Gradually the vision began to fade and I found myself back within Aileen's familiar room high above London's traffic, under the gentle gaze of my spirit mentor, who began to speak. "That was a spiritually rewarding lifetime my son, but one which was easy to follow, for there was little challenge. You were at all times protected from the harsh realities of life by the walls of the monastery, in which there was a complete absence of temptation, both carnal and material. You died with great knowledge, possessing the ability to be aware of your next incarnation and the Karmic debts you still had to redress. The Brothers Tsung-Li and Lien-Su were indeed a part of your past; Lien-Su was once your brother Mnas-Ra and your aid during this lifetime proved invaluable to him. Tsung-Li you will encounter upon your path later in this current lifetime."

"And Llama Tsien?" I enquired eagerly.

Here Wen Shu indicated Aileen. "None other than your beloved teacher."

Aileen looked somewhat surprised at this comment, not as yet being aware of what had been revealed to me.

Smiling at her, Wen Shu continued: "That, my son, completes the cycle of lives within which you studied the healing art. I will return at a later date to reveal one further lifetime."

With this, he raised his hand in farewell and faded from view.

Chapter 26

For many weeks Aileen and I discussed the numerous points raised in Wen Shu's appearances and wondered what the final lifetime he spoke of could possibly be. We both waited in eager anticipation for the completion of the tale. Yet it was a communication of a different kind which took place next. Sitting together in a deep meditation, we both became aware that the Brothers had joined us. Their appearances in the past had always been an indication of future happenings and my heart sank. 'What now?' I wondered, not wishing to vision further gloom and despondency.

The Atlantean Teacher spoke first: "You are correct in your assumption. It is indeed time for a further revelation. This is vital, for it relates to a land within which you must labour long during your current lifetime."

My curiosity aroused, I asked: "What land is that?"

The penetrating gaze of the Atlantean met mine. "We speak of the continent of Africa. It is time to journey, so please make yourself ready."

Gazing apologetically at Aileen, I entered into the silence and slowly the mists of time closed about us once more.

As these cleared, we hovered over a continent so vast that I could not envisage how I could possibly work there. Egypt, which formed a part of this great land, had always acted as a magnet to me, yet somehow I doubted that this was the land to which the Atlantean had referred. Here he interrupted my train of thought.

"The land you see beneath you is one much abused by the Aryan races. For long they have plundered its riches, carving great colonies out of its lands, totally ignoring the tribal and racial outlooks of the peoples. This cannot continue and the Aryan races will suffer the consequences of their earlier misdeeds. Those long held in bondage are about to rise against them and woe betide those with a fair skin during these times of change."

At this I interrupted him. "I realize that what you say is true, the white races, particularly my own, have much to answer for, but why must it happen now?"

He gazed at me thoughtfully. "The passing of the Age of Pisces, the age of emotional interchange, during which illusions were often pursued with greater gusto than the reality, will lead eventually to an age of enlightenment wherein all nations will come together as one, of their own volition. Before that may take place, all that which has been welded together under coercion, must break apart. Such happenings must, by their very nature, set in motion great suffering. All Mankind will seek their individuality, their opportunity to put their point of view, and to participate in the outcome. There will always be wars upon your planet until Man accepts the true concepts of brotherhood. Until then the strong will attack the weak, but in the long term such force will fail. Only that which comes about through the loving understanding of all peoples can last. Whilst Mankind continues to base his judgement upon concepts of race and creed, there cannot be peace upon your planet. Many of these concepts are so rigidly enforced that if they were not to be broken apart at this time, they would destroy the growth of the race of Man for all time. Such action is now imminent and you are about to vision a portion of it."

"Do you seek to imply that we shall one day have world government, based upon a concept of brotherhood of Man?" I asked. "Wen Shu has spoken in the past of the Race of Tan. Is this implied in your statement?"

He gave a small smile. "Indeed I do, for during the Age that the planet is about to enter, world government is not only envisaged, but it will be absolutely vital. In the dim past such forms of government have existed, but only on a minor scale. The tasks which lie ahead of Man will prove the validity of such a form of government. Before that day dawns, nationalism will become the rallying call, world wide. In itself, this is an extremely narrow point of view which excludes all else and bears within it the seeds of greater dissolution and disaster. Here in the continent of Africa, particularly, you will see a great rise in nationalism as the tribes become determined to make their voices heard. They will be equally determined to become recognized in their own right, being prepared to fight to achieve it. In so doing, old scores will be settled, enabling the Cosmic Pattern for the planet — and this continent in particular — to reach fruition. Sadly, it is only in this manner that Mankind will become aware of the need for universal brotherhood. The melding of the world's races will commence, producing eventually, the Race of Tan."

He paused awhile to note the effect of his words upon me, then resumed his explanation: "In common with all other lands, this continent will not escape the great geophysical changes. It is a vast continent, as you have noted, but pause awhile, let time elapse, and now take note . . . ."

The mists swirled about us and we appeared to be caught in some form of vacuum, then as the mists began to fade I watched with some fascination the land below us which appeared to be heaving and falling, great plains being rent apart, and as the land parted, enormous fissures appeared. Regardless of national boundaries and frontiers, the land was being swiftly dissected, great rivers changing their course in the twinkling of an eye, some of these now cascading into the fissures within the earth, vanishing on the instant into the very bowels of the earth, only to be cast heavenward in a short space of time in the form of steam.

From coast to coast, the changes went on, the seas themselves finding entry into what had been great arid plains, the confused and terrified wildlife being swept away in the resultant torrent. The temperature itself appeared to have undergone a great change, the life forms were now more abundant, much of the dust bowls were beginning to support a varied form of vegetation — the kind one was accustomed to noting in the more temperate zones. Still the earth tremors continued; the time lapse must have been enormous, although all this passed before my eyes in a very short space of time. As these began to subside, it was a vastly different continent which now lay before me. It was almost as though some gigantic being had rent the continent apart, and instead of one large continent there were now three separate stretches of land, each separated from the other by sea.

Gazing at me the Atlantean said quietly: "All of this will take many years to accomplish, but what you now see is the shape of things to come upon this continent. Now we must journey to a portion of this vast land, where we will require you to labour in the field of loving service during this current life span. Here you will share the healing gifts with Mankind, proving to those who are prepared to seek, the power of the Creator to restore Man to full health. However, even there they must be prepared for the changes to come. Incarnated within this continent are those who are to aid the transition of many from the narrow confines of a third dimensional outlook to the broader concepts of a fourth dimensional outlook."

Soon we were hovering over a truly beautiful coastal city. High in the background towered a majestic mountain, its top appearing to have been flattened at some point in time. As I observed the peaceful scene, the sky darkened and I was aware of a growing wall of sound. Following the direction of the sound, I saw a gigantic wave speeding towards the coast. Before I could cry out, the wave fell upon the city itself; mesmerized, I noted that it crushed the roofing of the majestic buildings, the inrush of water then bursting the buildings apart, destroying all within them.

The wave retreated as swiftly as it had appeared, taking with it the debris of the once fair city, leaving behind carnage and total chaos. Before I could speak, the Atlantean pointed away out to sea. "Observe," he said tersely. Soon, another enormous wave was speeding towards the coastline, another city in its path. Wave after wave crashed down upon the shores, decimating the population and buildings, leaving a trail of havoc in their wake.

"But why? Why?" I mouthed.

Shaking his head sadly he answered: "Each and every land must first be cleansed and then repopulated with those who will follow the ideal of the new Age. This land is not alone in its suffering. It has strong and vital energies which must be capitalized upon. Man will have need of them in the period which lies ahead. We will now return to your present time, for there is little more that I wish you to observe for the present. Note well the happenings today, for you will have to share this experience with those of that land who are prepared to note their true path and the path of their nation at the latter part of this century."

Here the mists closed around us once more and I soon found myself back with my beloved Aileen, the Brothers having departed.

Chapter 27

Following these revelations we were left alone for some considerable time. During this period Aileen suggested that we gather the information together and write it down in an endeavour to find a pattern; something by which we could indicate a time scale. This took some weeks, much of that related having faded into the dim regions of my mind. Continually Aileen had to exhort me to dig within my subconscious to produce an item which had been stored — or blotted from my conscious memory.

"It is very strange, nearly all the revelations indicate changes taking place in a geophysical manner, yet Nostradamus indicated world war for the end of the century," commented Aileen, once our task was completed.

"Yes, that puzzles me too, for the sections of the Bible the Brothers told me to read also spoke of wars." I looked at her hopefully. "Do you think that perhaps the earthquakes will replace the wars? Perhaps Nostradamus got it wrong?"

She shook her head gravely. "I very much doubt it, but we can always hope. I would not wish to see another world war."

I suddenly remembered something that the Atlantean Teacher had said: 'You will have much to remember the Moslems for later in this century.' I explained this to Aileen. "I wonder what he meant by that?" I said. "Perhaps we can ask him?"

Aileen chuckled. "Well, if you shout loud enough, perhaps he will answer! The Brothers certainly have the most disconcerting way of appearing when we talk about them."

Suddenly, almost as though summoned by that comment, Wen Shu appeared.

"Oh!" said Aileen, "we were expecting the other chap . . . ."

Wen Shu smiled at her. "The Brothers will appear soon," he said, "I came in advance to prepare you both."

Not having seen Wen Shu for some time I was naturally happy to have his company. "We have been collating the information given over the years, Wen Shu, and really do need the answer to some questions."

He beamed at me. "We are aware of your thought patterns, but felt it was vital for you to reach some conclusion before we returned."

"Will there be wars ahead Wen Shu, as the Bible states — and as Nostradamus predicted?" I asked reluctantly.

Looking thoughtfully at us both before answering, he replied: "Sadly, this may come to pass, largely through the indifference of Man for his brother."

"Now what exactly do you mean, Wen Shu — and what is the connection with the Moslems?" I asked.

Bidding us be comfortable he began his reply: "The last world war should have taught Mankind many valuable lessons, based as it was upon the narrow views of the few and great injustice for many. Sadly, at its end, the injustice begun within that war continued long after, none being prepared to resolve the situation at its heart."

He paused a moment, then continued: "The persecuted race, seeking a final home, set out to achieve this through force, all other means having failed. Your own race failed in its duty, my son, eventually leaving a situation wherein the persecuted found a promised land and those that they displaced were left to wander in the wilderness. For more than your biblical generation these souls have rotted without hope, abandoned by all, and in their midst a dreadful canker has arisen. Resentment and a deep sense of injustice, coupled with knowing that there is a callous indifference to their plight, are currently fermenting within these people the seeds of rebellion which will one day inflame the continent of Europe."

I sat dumbfounded at this. "Do you refer to the Palestinians?"

He nodded his head in agreement. "With the raising of the

standard of Islam will come the unleashing of great forces long held in abeyance."

I was somewhat disconcerted by his comments. "But the Arab world is notorious for its inability to unite, they are forever fighting amongst themselves."

His face shadowed with sadness he replied: "Like so many, my son, you judge without the benefit of foresight. Also you judge without the full realization of the force of faith. Once it is ignited it can unite people of widely diverging shades of opinion. If ignited by those who seek to sweep aside that which they have grown to hate, then naught can stem its flow."

Silenced by his comments, I awaited further enlightenment.

"However, the Brothers wish to instruct you on this point, so shall we await their coming?" he asked. We both nodded assent, a little apprehensive of that which now lay ahead. As we sat quietly the Brothers began to appear and we were soon surrounded by the familiar half circle of Brothers clad in their simple white robes. As usual, they deferred to the Atlantean Teacher, whose features were grave as he spoke.

"It is time to make you aware of the suffering that may be set in motion upon the planet by the thoughtless actions of Mankind," he started. "Some of that which we must reveal is almost too late to prevent, the ruling nations being unable or unwilling to take positive action. A great deal may be prevented if you and others like you can muster sufficient support in the task of healing the planet. Much responsibility lies upon your shoulders in this respect. In the event that you are unable to encourage a change in the direction of Man's thought patterns, it is vital for you to be aware of the consequences. You must use this information as you see fit. Use it, if you must, as the means of breaking down the negative thought patterns of those who wilfully disregard the truth."

Unable to comment, I awaited his next move.

"We must take you once more into the future," he continued, "much that you see there has already happened, created by the negative thought patterns of those who seek power above all else."

As his words echoed in my mind, the mists closed about me and the sound of rushing wind filled my ears; as the mists cleared, we hovered over a desert region, in the distance of which hills filled the far horizon. Great clouds of dust rose into the air, set in motion by a vast array of tanks which rumbled their way towards distant cities. Never before had I seen so many tanks.

"Come, let us move in the direction of the hills," said the Atlantean. As we approached these, a vast army was to be seen pouring over the heights, engaging in fierce conflict with defending forces. Overhead, missiles were hurling their deadly force towards the populated cities on the horizon. On all sides, tanks and brigades of troops were steadily advancing, the defending army being forced to retreat under the onslaught of the united attack.

"Where are we?" I demanded.

Speaking softly the Atlantean replied: "This is the land of Israel."

I was astonished, "But that is one of the best armed countries in the world! There is no Arab nation which is more heavily defended."

He nodded in agreement. "No single nation, I agree. But this is the united force of many nations. Below you see the combined forces of the Palestinians, armed at great cost by the Great Bear. Also with them march the armies of Libya, Persia and Ethiopia, all united in their determination to smash the power of Zion."

Awestruck, I watched the great conflagration of massed humanity below. "How many are there?" I asked, for on all fronts great armies were being poured into the conflict.

His succinct reply came rapidly: "Some two hundred million in all. Armed with their faith they will not be halted by military means."

Staring at him in horror, I gasped out: "But what will happen? Surely the Israeli nation cannot be wiped out in this manner?"

He returned my look impassively and said: "Watch and observe closely."

The battle below raged as settlement after settlement fell before the invading forces; none was spared, the most horrific scenes of bestial brutality unfolded before my eyes. Forced to retreat, the defenders fled before the onslaught, with no apparent coherent plan. Soon, however, wave upon wave of missiles filled the air taking their toll of the invading forces and their weaponry. Into the attack swept many squadrons of fighter planes which created havoc upon the ground. The attackers replied in force and the skies were soon filled with a conflict which rivalled the scenes taking place on the surface.

"But where are the United States forces in all this? And where are the forces of the United Nations? Where are they all?" I pleaded in an agonized tone.

Not looking at me he replied: "The United States is reeling under attacks of a different kind, for it has been swept by famine and experienced a great loss of land. They cannot attend to the needs of others."

"And the United Nations? What of them?" I asked urgently.

He shook his head. "They are racked with disagreement, the Arabic nations preventing reasoned discussions. Europe is also counting the cost of natural tragedies. Whilst Europe is in disarray, the forces of Islam have attacked."

Returning to the conflict with a grim fascination I watched the battle rage back and forth over the land. It appeared to continue for many months, the attackers never losing their ferocity and the defenders hanging on with grim determination. In the midst of this, great earthquakes took place, the mountains collapsing and taking with them many of the attacking forces who had used them to gain advantage. Elsewhere, the earthquakes took their toll, the forces of nature coming to the aid of the beleagured nation. Seizing the advantage given in this period, the forces of Zion swept into the attack, wave upon wave of fighter bombers inflicting tremendous destruction on the dazed attackers. From that point on the direction of the conflict changed, with many fleeing in the direction they had come. A great many fled in boats in the direction of the Red Sea, but hurricane force winds whipped up the waters capsizing even the largest vessels and bringing to a swift end the remnants of the conflict.

Not to be outdone, however, the forces of Zion swept over the borders of the neighbouring lands, dealing a swift and deadly blow to those who had supported the attack, before retreating to re-erect their badly shattered defences. Turning to the Atlantean I asked, puzzled: "Where did they obtain their arms? Even with their oil millions I cannot see where they procured such a lethal armoury."

Grimacing, he replied: "The Great Bear has long held plans for world supremacy. This is the beginning of that plan's fulfilment. They have duped the homeless refugees, who in turn have stimulated the fervour in others. What you see before you is the result of long and patient scheming on the part of the Land of the Great Bear, capitalizing on the hardships of others. As I stated earlier, nothing unites a people more than faith, particularly when stirred to attack an alien faith."

Placing his arm around my shoulders the Atlantean said: "Come, we must return for a while to your present time in order that we might discuss that which you have seen."

With this, the mists closed about us, the sound of rushing wind returned and somewhat dazed I found myself back at Aileen's feet, the Brothers around us as before. All sat quietly gazing at me, Aileen eagerly awaiting news of the journey. It was some time before I spoke, unable to frame the questions in my mind.

"Why Israel? Why so many forces against them?" I finally stammered.

Wen Shu answered first: "It has long been predicted, my son. You need only refer to your holy book for confirmation of that. As to why it must occur — why does Man make war against his brother? Greed; fear; a desire for total power — all of these negative emotions are involved in this conflict."

"But why the Jews? Have they not suffered enough?" I asked in despair.

He pondered my question before replying: "In one sense, perhaps, you are correct, but in part the people of Zion are responsible for this onslaught. Led by individuals of rigid outlook, they maintain a strong hold over the hapless inhabitants of the region. If over the years since the recreation of the State of Israel there had been a more considerate attitude towards the Palestinians, this would not be taking place. Man suffers for that which he sets in motion."

I gazed helplessly at them, unable to accept this point of view in totality. "Surely there are faults on all sides?"

The Atlantean leaned forward: "But of course. However, this time, the situation is made much worse by the involvement of major forces who seek world domination. In addition to this, one of the many anti-Christs will emerge during this period to ferment discord. All the participants are caught up in the vortex of a destructive force set in motion by the race of Man over many centuries. This is part of the great cleansing."

For some time I pondered upon what had been said and what I had seen. Turning to the Atlantean Teacher I asked: "Why the involvement of natural forces in this conflict? It appeared that they saved the Israeli forces from almost certain annihilation. Why was this?"

Gravely he replied: "It is not intended to destroy that nation, merely that it be taught to come to terms with those around and about it. They cannot remain aloof from the suffering of those within and about their borders; there must be a greater appreciation of the needs of all races, not simply their own. Nationalism has by necessity played a dominant part in the outgrowth of the state, now it must be tempered by a more tolerant outlook and a growing awareness of the need to share their frontiers with others."

I replied hotly: "That is all very well, but many of the neighbouring states are not prepared to allow them to live in peace . . . ."

Waiting for my fervour to cool, he replied: "Those states will soon fill their bellies with conflict and will learn many a bitter lesson. Of this you will soon be made aware."

"When you speak of the Great Bear, I take it that you do refer to the land we know as Russia?" I asked. The Atlantean nodded assent. "Then where were their forces during the conflict?" I questioned, curious to know more details.

He replied gravely: "At that time, world opinion will go against them and they will seek to use others in the conflict. In addition, they will have a greater quarry in their sights."

"And what might that be?" I asked with great interest.

"The Land of the Ancient Mysteries, where the great Sphinx stands on guard, ever watchful," came the unexpected reply.

I started up in amazement. "Egypt! But why?"

With a grim smile he answered: "It has vast lands, it controls much of the world's ocean-borne trade through its great artery — it is a great prize."

I could only gaze at him weakly. This was a land which had

played a great part in my past and it drew me still; why must this happen, I wondered?

Wen Shu had noted my thoughts and replied: "It will not succeed. In turning their attention to a Moslem country they will invite the wrath of all Islam. The viper they have nurtured within their breasts will strike at them and the Great Bear will be humbled."

This was astonishing to me, for no western nation had been able to defeat Russia during my lifetime. "Are you serious? How can that be?"

Wen Shu smiled at my reaction. "The forces of the Great Bear will be greatly stretched. They will be facing tumult in all the lands they hold in subjection. Unable to focus all their might in one spot, they will be hard pressed on all fronts, leading eventually to an uprising within their own land. Those suppressed for decades will seek the right to free expression, long denied them. Their power will crumble and the people will turn toward ancient faiths, rejecting for all time rigid and narrow outlooks which denied existence of the Creator."

I was somewhat puzzled by the continued reference to Islam as an organized power and said as much. This was greeted with a sad smile from the Atlantean Teacher, who said: "There will grow within those nations which have long been under the influence of Islam, a new energy. One will arise who will lead his people to overturn those in the seat of power and who will even challenge the mightiest nations. Defiant in the face of all threats, they will seek to widen their power base until they control all of the lands which face the European countries of the Mediterranean Sea. This will not be such a difficult task as you may imagine, the seeds of discontent have long been sown in those lands. One man, possessing a charismatic power and having total disregard for human life, will use his acquired wealth to furnish him with his desired power base. Millions will flock to his call and the scene will be set for those hordes to flow across the seas to vanquish the European lands. In this they will have the full backing of their Marxist allies."

Here I felt that I must interrupt. "But you have just stated that the Russians would be humbled by the Moslem countries. Why would they then back them in such an attack on Europe?"

His firm gaze held mine. "I did not refer to the Land of the

Great Bear. There is another mighty nation which is dominated by the belief of Marxism."

I stared at him in disbelief. "Do you mean China? Surely not."

He replied seriously: "The Land of the Dragon vies with the forces of the Great Bear for the support of the emerging nations. They lack not manpower and this would be supplied to any nation which requested it."

This was a point of view I had not before considered. Always the finger of accusation had been pointed towards Russia, few even considering China as an opposing force in world conflict. They had for some years sought to counter the influence of Russia in African states I realized, but would they really go this far?

Obviously well aware of my thought patterns, Wen Shu took my hand in his. "They will indeed, my son, for they are the last aspect of the final Atlantean race, the Mongols. Indeed, their last opportunity for world domination will present itself during the latter portion of your current century and they will take it determinedly."

Swallowing hard, I asked: "What then can we expect?"

Glancing towards the Atlantean Teacher he replied: "I feel perhaps you ought to vision the outcome, in order that you might fully understand."

My heart sank as the Atlantean nodded in agreement and I was filled with foreboding, for I had never had a very strong stomach for bloodshed, but I was certainly being subjected to more than my fair share this day. I reluctantly agreed with them and sat once more in the meditation position, awaiting the coming of the now familiar mists.

Soon we were flying high above countries which had a familiar look about them. "This is Southern Europe," said the Atlantean, in answer to my unspoken thought. "Let us draw closer." As we swooped down, many vessels were visible setting out from the coastline opposite. They were not battleships as I had expected, but strongly resembled large fishing vessels. Some of these made for a series of small islands, upon which they disgorged their cargo of destruction.

"Which islands are those?" I asked apprehensively.

"Those of Malta and her sister islands. Those in power

played with forces they did not understand, now their peoples will reap the sad harvest," was the reply.

"But cast your gaze further — the forces are now landing on the islands of Sicily and Sardinia, and soon upon the Italian mainland." As the Atlantean spoke I watched grim-faced as wave after wave of the vessels sped across the Mediterranean, apparently without end. They swiftly set ablaze the lands they alighted upon, although they did not have vast armaments; churches and monasteries, even the nunneries were all attacked. The populace were totally unsuspecting and were taken completely unawares. Those who would not make obeisance to Allah were butchered, including women and children.

It seemed that once begun there was no end to the tumult. There were larger forces joining the conflict now. Taking their toll were airborne raids which had now widened to take in Southern France and portions of Spain as well. Missiles now filled the air, hurtling towards their destination with a grim precision. The full force of the attacks switched to Southern France, with the port of Marseilles coming in for the greatest destruction. Wave after wave of missiles poured into that area, leaving little standing. All shipping in that great port was destroyed at the quaysides, mighty vessels sunk at their moorings or overturned, blocking the extensive waterway.

The Atlantean interrupted at this point. "Come, we must move in another direction." Soon we hovered over the once beautiful city of Paris. Like Marseilles, this was under bombardment from the air, and here also, many vessels were wrecked. Those who had sought to flee from the conflict via the Seine were destroyed before they travelled far. The air here was thick and choking. Indeed, the populace were falling where they were, clutching their throats, unable to breathe. The Atlantean was grim-faced. "The missiles are filled with a choking nerve gas. The people cannot survive. However the true centre of this conflict is elsewhere. Let us journey there."

We left the scene of horror and journeyed towards Italy once more. Here a great naval bombardment was taking place on the sea in the region between Rome and Genoa. By this time the Italian navy was under way and was fighting back strongly, but overhead the battle was being won in the air as waves of fighter jets swooped down upon the helpless cities.

"Why is Italy the main centre of this conflict?" I asked, unable to understand the logic behind it all.

"There are two major reasons," replied the Atlantean. "Italy is an old foe of the land behind this attack, and of course they seek to topple the Church of Rome. If they achieve this, then Islam will rule the world."

I was somewhat stupefied by his remarks. "But this is almost like the twelfth century, only the conflict is much worse! Why is this so?"

Shaking his head sadly he replied: "Man's inability to understand that although he may bear many names, there is but one Creator. The ignorance of Man is being manipulated here by those who serve another force. Times and weapons may change, but the underlying forces are the same. The time of darkness is upon the Earth."

"How long will all this last?" I finally managed to ask when I had controlled my sense of fear.

"For many years will the forces of darkness flow back and forth over the lands of Europe, for there is no one who will be able to withstand them."

"But what of England — and the United States, surely they would not stand idly by?" I said passionately.

He shook his head. "The land of your birth, controlled at that time by forces closely allied in thought and ideals fo the Marxist doctrine, will hesitate to become involved. Its armies will be greatly depleted by that time. They will eventually enter the fray — but too late. The United States will still be endeavouring to resolve her own problems."

The thought that my own land could possibly be controlled by Marxist sympathizers was one I could hardly envisage. The land of free speech dominated by that form of ignorance — why? How?

Wen Shu interrupted my train of thought at this point. "Mankind seeks power for differing reasons. Man's desire for power is the true source of evil within your plane of matter. For those who have not yet evolved spiritually, who have no true concept of the purpose of life, Marxism offers a near perfect ideology. Sadly, once they have obtained power, they are drawn to others with similar power and the corruption begins.

M

They lose sight of their ideals in the battle to retain the power — and the illusionary trappings it brings with it." Shaking his head sadly he continued: "There is much Man must absorb before he is fit to enter into the new Age of enlightenment."

At this point the Atlantean Teacher bade us journey to another location, where we might observe the continuing conflict. As I gazed down I noted a mighty army from neighbouring Yugoslavia marching relentlessly towards Italy. As I watched in horrified silence, this army cut a swathe of death through Northern Italy, determinedly making for Rome, which they proceeded to sack, even setting the Vatican ablaze. Touching my arm, the Brothers then indicated another vast army setting out from the area of China, and yet another from Turkey.

"Where are they headed?" I ventured to ask.

"France — the great city of the Republic will fall under their weight of arms," was his grim reply.

"But surely they have created more than sufficient havoc in that land, why further forces?" I asked in agonized tones.

"It is written," was his terse reply, "the people of France must pay for the blind adherence to nationalism, and an equally blind adherence to an outworn doctrine."

I shuddered at his words. "I think I have seen more than enough for the present — please, may we?"

Looking at me sternly he replied: "Of course — but there is still much for you to learn."

Soon the mists closed about us, thankfully blotting out the scenes of horror and I found myself back in Aileen's room.

Chapter 28

For many days I could not bear to be alone with my thoughts. I sought company, music, laughter — anything to take my mind off what I had been made to observe. I refused to accept that any of that could possibly happen — it must not. There was no valid reason. The more I endeavoured to push the matter from my mind, the more insidious it became. Eventually I had to seek out my beloved teacher and discuss the matter with her, for I had refused to speak of the happenings when I had finally returned to consciousness.

Feeling weak and exhausted after relating the dreadful tale, I gazed at her beseechingly. "What can we do Aileen? Surely it cannot come to pass? Please tell me it cannot."

She shook her head despondently. "What can I say? I have no vision. You must ask the Brothers."

I shuddered. "Oh no, they will only show me more of that — I just could not take any more."

Shaking me roughly she replied, "Oh come now, it will not help if you become an ostrich. Burying your head in the sands of time will not help anyone. Get a grip on yourself. You have a task to complete — as we all have. Let us summon the Brothers."

Feeling powerless to refuse although in my heart I feared further contact, we sat in meditation. Soon, the atmosphere became charged with a loving light as Wen Shu made his appearance before us. Gazing at me with deep love he did not comment, being content to radiate a force which entered into my very being, seeming to recharge me and aiding my return to a more positive frame of mind.

"It is never easy, my son," he said, "to observe the fearful conflicts which Man sets in motion upon the planet. Had you enjoyed the scenes I would have feared for your future. It is, however, necessary for you to be aware of all the ignorance that Man can set in motion. Much of that which you visioned can be lessened if the race of Man will accept the need to change itself. The answer, as ever, lies within Man himself. None of this need take place."

I nodded, remaining quiet, unable to speak. Seeing this, he said: "There are many questions within your mind which we feel should be resolved before we continue with further revelations. It is for that reason I have drawn close, in order that I might attempt to clear them for you."

My eyes filled with tears I could only nod in agreement, for my mind was bursting with questions of all kinds, but it was difficult to frame them. He sat quietly, awaiting my response, gently beaming love towards me.

"Why . . . why is France to be so badly devastated? She seems to be the target for the major destruction . . . why?" I asked at last.

He answered, his voice full of sadness, "That nation must play a great part in the spiritual outgrowth of the race of Man in the new Age. As you have been instructed earlier, there are many incarnate within that land who brought with them great knowledge and inner awareness from earlier life experiences. Sadly, they chose to subdue these, following nationalism and dogmatic faith, robbing the people of a deeply intuitive leadership. Such blind actions have opened the way to the cleansing forces of destruction. But she will rise again and assist many within the new Age to appreciate harmony in all things; design, colour, and the arts."

"It seems an excessive repayment to me," I commented with some heat.

He gazed at me quietly, but did not comment.

"Why were so many armies in motion — and so many coming from the areas currently controlled by Russia? Why? China also — this I do not understand," I said, as I continued my questioning.

Wen Shu gave a profound sigh. "It is the time of the Mongols. Their land will be greatly ravaged by natural disasters, they will need to find new methods of filling their rice bowls. Also, as the satellite states throw off the yoke of the Great Bear, the Land of the Dragon will advance, offering assistance, but in fact, will be seeking to replace the Great Bear as their overlord."

"And England — it was said that she would enter the fray, but too late. What exactly was meant by that?" I enquired.

His sigh was profound. "Only when it is too late to prevent the conflict will England and France awaken to the greater threat posed to their continued existence. Together they will muster their armies and move towards the seas off Italy, where the major conflict will be under way. However, the enemy armies will outflank them and strike into Southern France, taking the port of Marseilles. Later, vast armies drawn from all of the conquered nations and now converted to the Moslem faith, will pour into France, conquering the whole land. Those who do not bend the knee to the new masters and the new faith will perish."

I sat aghast, unable to utter a word. He continued: "But the hordes will not stop there. They have their eyes set on even greater prizes: Switzerland, with its vast storehouses, will be ransacked, and Germany will reel under the boot of the conquerors."

I gazed at him sadly. "It is not a very pleasant picture that you paint Wen Shu — what will become of the race of Man?"

A sweet smile creased his face, illumining it. "All is not yet lost, my son. Always there will arise one who will seek to smite the forces of darkness. There will be such a soul to lead Mankind forward."

My being filled with delight at this comment and the words tumbled eagerly from my lips: "Really? There will be a way out? Truly?"

He nodded in agreement. "Of course, my son, you must not believe the tales that tell of the destruction of Mankind and the end of the planet; that is not foreshadowed."

Excitedly I asked: "Tell me . . . tell me . . . who will this man be?"

Chuckling at my swift change of outlook he answered: "This will be a General, one who is as cunning as those he seeks to overcome. One who has incarnated for this purpose. He will instil determination to overcome within those who follow him, and they in turn will fight with just as much fury and barbarity as those who oppose them. Unused to such retaliation, the Moslem-controlled hordes will be shaken and put to flight. A major success will be the capture, at sea, of the senior Marxist General, which will rob the Moslems of much of their campaigning strength."

"But who will this man be? What country will he come from?" I asked, eager for further knowledge of this new leader.

"He will be found in the low-lying regions of Europe, determined to fight not only for his country, but also for his faith. Once again, it will be faith which will ignite the armies, providing the Europeans with that which they had hitherto lacked."

"Yes, yes, but what is his name?" I asked impatiently.

Wen Shu shook his head. "There is no need for names or titles at this time. He will know when his time is ripe. Then all the world will know his name."

Somewhat deflated at this reply I asked quietly: "What will be the final outcome?"

He smiled understandingly at me. "Once this General has put to flight all the forces of Islam, he will set about re-establishing the Christian faith in Europe. So many, through fear, will have become converted to Islam and these will now happily return to the old, old, faith. There will be a return to a balanced life, for this General will, throughout his career, move at all times under the guidance of spirit forces. His success in battle will cause him to be made King over Europe, for he will prove to be the only valid leader. For many years peace will exist under his reign."

I gave a deep sigh of relief. "Thank goodness for that, at least we can look forward to peace in the long term."

He glanced at me quizzically. "I did not state that this would be the end of all conflict."

I glanced sharply at him, something in the tone of his voice making me apprehensive. "But . . . you said . . . ."

He shook his head. "I merely stated that for some years, peace would exist under his reign. There is still the possibility of a major conflict ahead."

My heart sank at these words. What more could happen to Man, I wondered? I glanced at him half-fearfully from under lowered brows, awaiting his explanation.

"Before we relate that portion, it is necessary for you to realize that even with all the information provided, you may still fail in your chosen role. I will return in the near future to reveal one further lifetime, in order to illustrate the pitfalls. Until that time I will take my leave of you both." With a benign smile, he promptly faded from view.

Chapter 29

It was with some trepidation that I made my way towards my teacher's home one week later. Having received a strong intimation from Wen Shu that it was time for the further journey into the past to commence, I sought out Aileen, feeling that in her company I would at least find strength. As we sat quietly discussing much that had transpired during the last session with Wen Shu, he swiftly made his noiseless appearance, causing Aileen to start visibly.

Smiling his greeting to us, he waved his hand, indicating that it was time for us to commence our journey. Sitting quietly at his feet I gazed up at him, wondering what was to be revealed today. Placing his hand upon my shoulder he said: "That which I am about to unfold relates to a life you chose deliberately in order to erase much negative Karma from your Akashic Record in a short space of time. It turned out to be far more difficult a task than you could have foreseen and you almost failed in the attempt. None the less, when in the depths of despair, full of bitterness and disillusionment, help was sent to you."

Placing his hands upon my upper Chakra points, he stimulated the now familiar feeling of light-headedness. As all about me swam before my eyes, he continued gently, "This was a life in the male form, centred in Spain during the Dark Ages, where you were one of many sons of a peasant farmer . . . ."

A scene of harsh experience began to unfold before my eyes. Life itself was concentrated around the land, rising with the dawn to till the stony infertile soil, tending the growing crops, hours of my childhood years spent in hard labour gathering in the harvest with my brothers. There was little joy in our lives. Dependent as we were upon the land for sustenance, it became the predominant force in our drab lives and one which we became resigned to. Only on Sundays was there any respite when, dressed in our humble best, we followed Father and Mother on the long journey to our local church. This consisted of a simple white adobe building, its interior relieved only by the great wooden crucifix which dominated the area above the altar.

There was little money to spare at the time of the great Christmas feast, our fun being derived from family games and horseplay indulged in by boys throughout the ages. As the smallest in the family, I often became the target for uproarious laughter as they made me the victim of these games, and one day I was thrown into the foul-smelling cess-pit. Their loud sounds of merriment soon brought Mother out of doors to find the source of their amusement and her look of horror at my appearance swiftly turned to anger directed at my brothers as she sought to cleanse me of the filth.

From that time on my health began to deteriorate and some two years later strange white patches began to appear on my hands. "Look Mamma — what are these?" I asked her curiously.

Stepping back in horror she swiftly made the sign of the cross. "Holy Mother of God, leprosy . . . ." She gazed at me, her eyes filled with fear, agitatedly moving away from me, suddenly afraid to touch the fruit of her womb.

"What is wrong Mamma? What is it?" I cried, deeply puzzled by her manner and actions.

She held her hand out to protect herself. "Keep away — keep away," she wailed. Pulling her apron over her head she ran from the kitchen crying: "Pappa . . . Pappa . . . ." I followed her slowly, not understanding, but with a growing feeling of rejection. I stared at the white patches upon my hands curiously. 'What could they be to cause Mamma to act in this way?' I thought.

Soon the whole family came to stare curiously at me, all maintaining a safe distance from me. Pappa edged forward slowly. "Show me your hands," he cried, his voice filled with fear, his body rigid. I slowly extended my hands so that all might see. Quickly crossing himself he muttered: "The curse — the curse . . . ." Suddenly, his eyes fixed upon my face, his expression hard, he said grimly: "You must leave — at once. You must leave."

I gazed at him dumbly, not understanding what I could have done to warrant this. "But why? What have I done?" I cried in terror.

Shaking his head at me he shouted: "Leave us — leave. You must go away, we do not wish to catch it."

Nonplussed I asked, "Catch what, Pappa?"

He pointed fearfully at my hands. "That! It is . . . leprosy . . . . You must leave my boy, you cannot stay here."

Gazing at him and then at my mother who stood transfixed in terror, I pleaded: "But where shall I go? How shall I live?"

He shook his head at me and answered implacably: "I do not know, but for the sake of your mother and your brothers you must leave."

My mother began to wail, sobbing into her apron, her thin frame racked with sobs. I stepped towards her, arms outstretched. My father stepped back hastily pulling Mother with him. "Keep away, keep away," he cried in a fearful tone, and again crossed himself. "Go!" he demanded. "Take some food with you, but go — please leave us, now."

Breaking down in tears I fell to the earth, begging him to allow me to stay, but to no avail, it was as if they had turned to stone. Finally I shakily stood up and miserably set about gathering some food, which I wrapped in my ragged blanket. Sadly I left my home, looking back constantly to see if there had been a change of mind on the part of my parents. My thoughts were confused; what must I do now? I could only think of the priest — he would help me, tell me what I must do. So I set out on the long journey, this time alone, with only my fears and sorrow for company.

On reaching the small church I began to beat upon the door of the little cottage which housed the priest. Some time elapsed before he answered my hammerings. "Good heavens Juan," he said, gazing at my tear-stained face, "whatever is wrong? Is it your father?"

I shook my head dully and held out my hands. He stepped back, his eyes filled with fear. "Dear Father God," he whispered, "leprosy!" Shaking his head in disbelief he asked sharply, "Why do you come here?"

Gazing at him beseechingly I faltered: "For help; help me Father. My family . . . ."

He stepped back within the cottage. "I cannot help you, no one can. You must go away."

"But what am I to do?" I screamed at him, my terror now equalling his fear.

"I cannot say — pray to the Lord that He may take this from you, Juan, but you must leave this area." He hastily slammed the door, bolting it after him.

I was alone, unwanted. I sank down in despair and sobbed heart-brokenly. What was I to do? Even the servant of the Lord had turned me away. None would help me, how was I to live? How long I lay there I had no idea, but with the falling of darkness the air turned chill and I knew I had to move my stiff body somehow. I stumbled off into the darkness and slept under a large boulder just outside the village.

The days turned into weeks, all filled with the pain of rejection. Those who had once enjoyed my company now looked at me with revulsion, all turning from me in fear. Some, who had kind hearts, threw crusts and scraps to me that I might eat, but none would come near me. Robbed of all human contact, it dawned on me how precious it was. None would share simple kindness, all now feared me. The weeks stretched into months and those into years and I grew steadily more bitter. The cess-pit. It had been the cess-pit. If my brothers had not tossed me in, this would not have happened. I now longed for the harsh life I had disliked; now, it seemed a glorious existence compared to that which I had been forced into.

I wandered far, for few would give me sufficient to stay alive and I was reduced to stealing from the fields in the dead of night, turning over the garbage in search of food, killing whatever I might to obtain sustenance. My features had now become grotesque as the scourge swept my body. My face was greatly eaten away and few cared to look upon me, all turning to run. I had by this time reached the outer walls of the great city of Granada. These towered above me and at night the gates were firmly locked to ensure that none could enter.

One night, hunting below the walls in my incessant search for food, I stumbled upon a small body. Turning it over eagerly, I began to search it for any item of value. As I did so, I felt a faint heart beat. The boy was not dead, although he had been badly beaten up. Gathering him up, I took him to my retreat, where I bathed his wounds. By the light of day I gazed at him with interest as he lay weak and helpless. "A gipsy by the look of him," I muttered to myself. Gipsies fared little better than I among the local populace and this one had evidently fallen foul of a group who had cast him out for dead.

As time passed his wounds healed, his strength returned, and I found he had become a friend. Although puzzled by my appearance, his love and gratitude for his deliverance were beyond measure. That in itself helped to heal the many wounds, for until he came I had often contemplated ending this futile life. From that point on we wandered the length and breadth of Spain, hounded wherever we went, but happy to be together. As he grew in strength and I grew weaker, he held my hand and led me, begging for alms and food, sustaining me to the end of a very sad life.

I felt the firm grip of Wen Shu's hand upon my shoulder as I returned to consciousness. I shuddered with revulsion at the memories still fresh in my mind. He smiled his gentle smile as I sat awaiting his comments. "With that life, the Lords of Karma granted you a test — and when all was dark and desolate, it looked as though you would fail in your life lesson. Circumstances, environment, and traits of characters, were all balanced against the chance of you showing mercy to that abandoned waif. However, the strength of your inner light prevailed. Upon the scale of Karmic Law, this life was a greatly rewarding one." His smile broadened as he continued: "That gipsy waif stands upon your path once more. You will encounter him during this lifetime. This time you must lead him towards inner awareness."

I gazed at him quizzically. "What was the purpose of revealing that unpleasant experience?"

He sighed as he replied: "To give you strength in the tests ahead of you. When once again all is set against you, when Man turns his face away, to know that you have been this way before — and have overcome. It should also teach you to value human contact and friendship, for within your character there is a trait which leads you to solitude. This has its roots in a different life, one which one day we may reveal."

Fear struck me with his words. "You say, 'when Man once again turns his face away'. Do you mean I am going to contract that disease once more?"

He shook his head and smiled, replying: "No, no, my son — although to some you may surely represent a leper when you come bearing sad tidings. You will disturb their materialistic shallowness and they will turn away from you, shun you even. You may also once again be driven to consider the most foul of deeds — suicide."

I stared at him intently. "Tell me about suicides," I said urgently.

"Why do you ask in that way?" he asked, staring placidly back at me.

"Because I have recently discovered that a dear friend of mine has taken his own life. What will happen to him?"

Pondering on my question for a while, he answered: "It would be far easier to take you to him, for it will provide a vital lesson. What is his name?"

I stared at him in amazement. Did I hear aright? He would take me to him? How? Finally I stammered, "His . . . name . . . was Neil."

"Good," he replied brusquely. "Can you picture him?"

"Yes," I replied hesitantly, "I think so."

"Good," he said, making a gesture for me to be seated. "Let us sit and concentrate upon him then."

I focused my thoughts upon my dear friend, whose tragic death had come as such a deep shock to me. As I began to focus his image within my mind I was aware of leaving my body and travelling swiftly through space. Soon we stopped before a high grey stone building. "This is a little grim," I said to Wen Shu.

He nodded. "This is the prison he has created for himself, for his wrongdoing."

I gazed at him in some astonishment. "You mean that this is just a thought form?"

"Oh yes," he replied, "and as solid as anything on your Earth plane to him."

"Can we locate him?" I asked eagerly.

He smiled at me in reply. "That is the reason for our journey, my son, in order that you may assist him. Now, let us enter."

We moved into the dank smelling fortress and wended our way downwards until we reached a dark dungeon. Gazing through the grill I saw Neil lying listlessly against one wall. "Neil! Neil!" I called excitedly.

Wen Shu grasped my arm. "He cannot hear you my son, you will have to focus your thought upon him in love; let him know that you forgive him."

I stared helplessly at him. "Forgive him? But I have nothing to forgive."

"In his mind there is, my son. Please do as I ask," he said patiently.

Feeling rather foolish I began to communicate with Neil in thought, sending out thoughts of love and telling him that he was forgiven for his hasty action. Slowly he turned towards me, his face bleak.

"Concentrate upon love, my son," whispered Wen Shu. As I did so, he slowly staggered to his feet, his face breaking into a smile of recognition, his hands reaching out towards me.

The door seemed to melt away and I held him in my arms as he sobbed: "I didn't mean to do it . . . I was so lonely . . . I felt I couldn't go on." Gazing at me beseechingly through his tears he begged: "You do forgive me, say again that you do."

"Of course I do, Neil," I said, overcome with emotion myself.

Wen Shu bent and again whispered in my ear: "Tell him that he need not stay here any longer — that he can accompany you to a more peaceful spot."

A little puzzled as to why he could not tell him, I did as I was bid. Neil pulled back sharply at this. "No, no, I must stay here — for ever. I . . . ."

"No, no, no! No, Neil," I cried, "you can leave now, you are forgiven. Please come with me." It took some considerable time to persuade him to leave that dank dungeon and to follow Wen Shu and myself out into the light.

Once outside, the scene had changed, much to my astonishment. We were on the perimeter of a beautiful garden, outside which stood a monk, his face filled with compassion. On seeing him, Neil stopped short. "Oh, it's you . . . ." The monk nodded and stretched out his hand to Neil, who grasped it firmly, turning to me as he did so. "I must go with my friend now — but you will come and see me again won't you, please?" I nodded through my tears as he was led into the garden. I rushed forward to see where he was going, only to find my way barred by a giant screen composed of a metallic substance, through which it was possible to observe Neil quite clearly.

The garden was a wonder to see, filled with tall graceful trees and verdant green lawns. A small fountain played its gentle music and the air was sweet. Turning to Wen Shu I asked: "What place is this?"

He smiled at me, saying: "It is that point wherein he must remain for some time to come. Here he will be encouraged to view his past life, to note his failings and to pass judgement upon himself. Later he will need to experience the pain and the suffering he has inflicted upon those he has left behind. The monk, who is his door-keeper, was familiar to him, as you noted. He will be his only contact from this time on, although you may come and communicate with him during your sleep-state journeyings. He needs your love and your thoughts of light. Without your help he will never make it."

"What will happen to him eventually?" I asked, somewhat puzzled.

"Much depends upon his reactions from this point on. He can remain here in solitude until his allotted Earth span is completed, or he can, after the purification process is complete, offer to aid others in the same situation. That must be his decision."

Impulsively I replied: "Anything I can do to help him I will; he was a very dear friend."

Wen Shu nodded. "The links between you travel through time. You were brother officers in the army of Rome, both being of Greek ancestry. Strong links were forged then, they will not be broken by time." Somewhat uplifted by his remarks I returned happily to consciousness to share the experience excitedly with Aileen.

Chapter 30

Within a week the Brothers returned to continue the tale for the future. I gazed at them somewhat apprehensively, for I really did not relish the thought of further destruction. Wen Shu smiled at me gently. "We must now complete the visioning my son. Over all, it will provide you with the strength you will require to fulfil your life's task."

Swallowing hard, I nodded in acknowledgement and prepared to enter the mists of time again.

Soon we were hovering over Europe once more. The enormous damage inflicted by the war was still clearly visible, although on all sides great rebuilding works were under way. We made our way to Italy and I noted that much of the land had vanished, having sunk beneath the waters which had now washed over what had been large coastal cities. Everywhere there was a new-found energy, as the people busied themselves with rebuilding their shattered lives.

The voice of the Atlantean sounded in my ear: "The great Warrior King is now drawing to the end of his reign, having re-established peace in all the lands of Europe, the hordes of Islam long silent. He has re-established the Christian faith and his government is closely allied to it; there has developed a deep bond between state and faith, with the Church playing a dominant role."

"Providing the Church is led by spiritually developed men, is that not a good thing?" I asked, looking at him questioningly.

He nodded grimly. "Until this time all has been well, but an evil canker grows in their midst: the final anti-Christ prepares to reveal himself."

I stared at him in horror. "You mean that such a soul has power within the Church?"

He gave me a speculative look. "It would not be the first time that men of the cloth sought ultimate power over their fellow men."

Realizing that he was of course correct, I said: "Tell me about this man — who is he?"

Bidding me sit beside him he answered: "He is one with strange beginnings, born of parents who were once staunch pillars of the Church of Rome, prior to the ending of that great war you so recently witnessed. He is by nature deceitful and cunning — the war encouraged these traits within him. He has come up within the Church, for that was all he knew. He projects a public image which has succeeded in fooling all. He now works his cunning upon the ruling faction, seeking to become heir apparent to the Warrior King."

I interrupted. "Surely that will not happen?"

Sadly, he nodded his head. "It must, for this is his hour.

When it comes he will soon reveal himself to be lustful and cruel. He will swiftly undo all the good created by the Warrior King whom he has now replaced.

"Come, let us journey forward a little in time," he bade me, and we set off once more into the mists. As these cleared we were in the remnants of the city of Rome. A vastly different city this, to that of my memories. Gone was the Vatican and the great churches. Much activity was centred around a refurbished Colosseum, where many were coming and going. I gazed at the scene rather mystified. The Atlantean answered my unspoken question. "It is now the seat of his public endeavours. He has set himself up as God — all must worship him as such, or perish."

I stopped in my tracks in sheer amazement. "As God? Surely no one would be so foolish as . . .?"

His ineffably sad features stemmed the tide of any further comments. "Indeed they would — in fear of their lives. Not only here, but throughout Europe the message has gone out, many are again bending the knee to the false prophet. Even now he seeks to confirm it for all the world to see. He is about to stage an Ascension into the heavens."

Totally dumbfounded I gazed at the scene below us. From all quarters the people were arriving, the building itself filling with the thousands of spectators, all come to witness this wondrous event. Soon with great fanfares of trumpets this arrogant man bedecked in all the finery of churchly splendour, his face hard and cruel, made his way into the great auditorium. Great cries of exultant joy rent the air as the assembled throng greeted their God incarnate.

Silence settled upon the gathered masses as he took his place upon a great carved throne erected in the centre of the auditorium. All waited expectantly for the miracle to take place. As this scene unfolded the land around the Colosseum began to shake violently; in the far distance, long-silent volcanoes erupted. The sky over the land became filled with the reflection of the resultant fires and the massive edifice of the Colosseum swiftly crumbled, burying all within it.

Earthquakes continued to shake the land, the seas around boiled and great waves poured over it. The land that was Italy began to break apart and strife erupted among the people of Earth. The conflict that I grimly witnessed was even more destructive than any I had seen before, for brother turned against brother, as the believers fought the non-believers.

Taking my arm in a firm grip the Atlantean commanded, "Let us return, we have witnessed sufficient." Thankfully I followed him into the mists and rejoined the Brothers and Aileen in her peaceful room. Quite unable to speak of what I had witnessed, although my mind seethed with a tumult of questions in connection with the scenes I had just visioned, I awaited his direction.

"That which you have witnessed was the end of the final anti-Christ," the Atlantean began. "His rule will be short, but during it he will set in motion seeds which will bring about a return of conflict to the planet. Men will fight among themselves as the forces of darkness seek to maintain their hold upon Mankind. The mighty Church of Rome will collapse, retaining but few followers, many greatly disillusioned by the actions of their papal leader. The Mongols will seek one final attempt at world domination and the world will once more erupt into conflict." Noting my anguished expression he said quietly, "But it will be the beginning of the end for the dark forces, for the Cosmic Christ approaches. All who bowed the knee to false gods and prophets will pay dearly for their folly. Those who remained steadfast, despite great suffering, will have cause for great rejoicing."

"What will bring about the end of the conflicts?" I asked hesitantly.

"The surface of the planet will erupt in divers places — earthquakes will dislodge and swallow the forces of war, Man will be left in no doubt as to who is the true ruler of the planet," he said firmly.

Swallowing hard I asked, "You spoke of the Cosmic Christ. Will He appear immediately — as a man?"

He shook his head. "The force of the Cosmic Christ must, by its very nature, approach the Earth slowly. As He does so, He sets in motion great energies which will cleanse the minds and hearts of Mankind. There will come a great Teacher who will be overshadowed by the Cosmic Christ. This Teacher for the new Age will not appear until the new century is well under way."

I gazed at him hopefully. "Where will He appear? Many say it will be Israel — is that so?"

N

His features softened slightly as he answered: "By the time the Teacher appears much will have changed upon your planet. In one sense you will have new heavens and a new earth, in as much as that a great deal of that which is inhabited today will then be deep below the oceans. New lands will be supporting Man, lands which are fresh, with vital energies for Mankind to build upon."

Deeply astonished at his words I asked: "What do you mean — 'new heavens and a new earth'? How can that be?"

He stared penetratingly at me. "Have we not instructed you that there will come a time when the magnetic poles of your planet will move again?"

Falteringly I replied: "Yes, you have — but . . . ."

"With the shift of your polar regions many lands will appear from beneath the waters and the ice, others will vanish or be covered by ice. With the change of your magnetic poles, the heavens themselves will appear to have altered."

I stared at him, for I had not contemplated this point of view. "Not much hope for Man in all that, is there?" I muttered.

"The better elements will be saved. All else will be swept away," he replied.

"Oh dear," I sighed, "and this is the message you wish me to share with others? They will lynch me!"

Giving me one of his rare smiles he answered: "That is the purpose of your incarnation, to make Mankind aware of the need for change in himself. If the warning is not heeded, then by necessity Man will have to undergo the terrible things you have witnessed."

Taking pity on me, Wen Shu intervened. "It does seem, my son," he said gently, "that in common with all others, you are ignoring the most important point here." I stared at him questioningly and he continued: "There is no death. Only rebirth — into reality. The most important lesson over all for Man, is to change his outlook — his destiny — through acceptance of the need to locate the God-force within and accept it as the Reality. Man will never find it within a false god or prophet. The scenes you have witnessed illustrate the depths Man will sink to in order to maintain his hold upon the illusionary world of matter. Your task is to teach them to understand the true nature of this third dimension, teach them to let go and to grasp the reality firmly in their hearts."

"That will be no easy task," I muttered, filled with a sense of impossible odds.

He chuckled at my despair. "It will not be easy, that is true, but you are more than capable of achieving this. Of course, there will always be those who are unable to loose their hold upon matter. When faced with the choice of letting go their illusionary possessions and saving themselves, many will cling to their tawdry belongings and be swept away in the resulting tide of war and destruction. You have only to gaze upon the refugees who pour out of your cities when war strikes. They weigh themselves down with their pitiful belongings, which in the long term they have to abandon, as their tenure on life becomes greatly weakened." Gazing at me for a moment, he carefully added, "During the not too distant future you too, my son, must learn to give up all possessions."

I stared at him, somewhat horrified. I was about to purchase my first home and I had for some years collected beautiful objects with which to furnish it. "All but ashes, my son," he said in answer to my thoughts. "Do not be caught up in them," he added warningly.

"Now we feel that you have much to consider and evaluate. Contemplate upon that which you have observed and if there are points you wish us to clarify, we shall be more than happy to return." Bowing low, he and the Brothers took their leave of us.

Chapter 31

The portents indicated by the Brothers left me in a mood of despair; even Aileen could see little light. What was the over-all purpose? I pondered for many hours, for it seemed that within that which I had been shown there was a pattern, something Man could build upon. Always the Brothers returned to thought patterns, destructive energies setting in motion that which engulfed the planet. How could we stop it? What was more important, where did it all lead? These and many other questions filled my days and it was obvious I had to contact the Brothers once more.

With Aileen's agreement, I decided to ask to look forward at what lay ahead of the planet beyond the conflict, for there had to be something upon which we might build our future. Sitting impatiently, my mind wandered over the many questions. So engrossed in them was I that I did not note the appearance of the Brothers.

"You have many questions, my son?" said Wen Shu quietly.

Startled, I sat upright. "Yes . . . yes I have, but I wish to ask if I may see beyond the strife — if there is anything beyond it?"

He smiled at me. "But of course, my son, that was always our intention. Come, prepare yourself and we will journey into the future."

Slowly I stilled my mind seeking to merge with the consciousness of the Brothers, and began to be aware of the mists around us once again. As these cleared, I gazed curiously down upon the scene before me. All was strange, the like of which I had not seen before. There was abundant growth and a great many tall trees, largely of the fruiting variety. As we hovered over the scene I noted we were approaching some form of civilization. My attention was drawn to vast antennae which stood upon the outskirts of the city. They seemed to oscillate with the wind, yet all was silent, no sound could be heard.

Moving on into the city I noted great beauty. The streets were filled with trees of every kind and great use had been made of water in the form of pools and fountains. The people were tall, having elongated skull formations. There was no visible stress, life seemed to be lived at a quiet pace. I gazed at the Atlantean, who as always on these journeys was close by my side. He said quietly, "Life is vastly different to that currently experienced upon the Earth plane. The people live in peace and harmony; they know not war — indeed they know naught of what went before, all has been expunged from their memories.

"Come, let us see how they deal with miscreants," he said. We travelled a little further and soon we arrived at an airy building built around a large pool. The area surrounding this was filled with flowering shrubs and trees, the atmosphere one of peace. "A great deal of difference to your current courts of Justice," he said softly. "Here will be found the city elders who will gently discuss the problems with the wrongdoers, offering advice. No threat or force will be used."

I looked at him questioningly. "How then will they change their ways?"

"It is quite simple," he replied, "they will be given a surfeit of that which they desire most." I was astonished at this, although the concept was not exactly new.

"But why?" I asked, deeply puzzled. Bidding me be seated he answered: "Man by this time has risen above the pull of illusionary matter, although there are still a few who demand money and possessions, seeking to take them from those who have them. In order to help them understand how foolish they are, they are given all they desire, whilst the remainder of the populace stand by greatly amused."

Shaking my head in sheer disbelief I answered: "Well, that is certainly a novel manner of dealing with the situation."

"Life has changed on Earth, all conflict is behind the race of Man," he said. "This edifice has replaced your courts and prisons. Also, there are no churches and no hospitals, Man being taught to find the God-consciousness within himself. Once he achieves this, there is no more sickness. Man is whole."

"Good heavens," I muttered, "it seems more like heaven on earth." A thought struck me. "What were those large antennae outside the city?"

Happy to note my interest he answered: "That is the manner in which they generate their power source. They use the wind itself to provide a free form of power. They also utilize water to provide another source of energy."

"The people — they are so different, so tall," I said. "Is this the new race?"

Nodding his head in agreement he answered: "It is the beginning. Greater and finer forms still await manifestation during this age of enlightenment. Also their lives are vastly different to yours. The people labour for but half of the year; in the spring-time to sow the crops, and in the autumn to reap

o

them. The remaining periods are spent in study and observing life elsewhere upon the planet."

"But who tends to the crops once planted?" I asked in disbelief.

A look of amusement crossed his face as he replied: "Others who rotate their free time accordingly. None labours more than six months in the whole year."

"What of the Christ for Aquarius — is He here? May I see Him?" I asked eagerly.

Shaking his head he answered: "The Great Teacher has been — and long since departed. His legacy to Mankind is working now upon the race of Man. He came not alone — for does not your holy book tell that He will come with His heavenly hosts?"

I nodded in agreement, and naïvely looked about me. "Where are they?" I demanded.

Amused by my question he replied: "They are not visible, for they have not Earth forms. They are beings of light, clad in a form of etheric light. They labour now to teach Mankind to transmute his physical form into light."

"How is that possible? And why?" I asked. In reply he looked at me for a moment or two consideringly then began to speak.

"Man," he said, "was not always physical, he first dwelt in etheric form, later taking on the heavier body of flesh. The planet is speeding towards the Jupiter Period, within which Mankind must dwell solely within a body of light, overseeing the change in lower forms of matter. This was the original purpose of incarnation."

"But how are they to transmute the body?" I asked, intrigued. "It all sounds like a vague alchemical process to me."

The Atlantean explained: "By total thought control. Coming to terms with matter, learning to spiritualize the form within which he is encased. It cannot be accomplished in one physical incarnation, of course. Life after life, they will have to continue the upward shift in their level of consciousness, until finally they achieve fourth dimensional awareness in the midst of a three dimensional world."

"It is not easy to contemplate," I answered.

Quietly he replied: "It is even more difficult to express in a manner that your mind can understand. It must be sufficient to realize that the new Age which lies beyond your current Age of Pisces will make giant strides in the evolutionary pattern. Man is not doomed, neither is the planet upon which he incarnates. Changes are inevitable, but in the long term there is much that will benefit Mankind."

We moved on, noting the tranquillity of the scene below us. The globe had certainly changed a great deal; so many of the familiar lands had changed dramatically or vanished. But there were new lands, large tracts of earth which sustained life, providing ample opportunities for the survivors of the human race.

"I think you have seen sufficient," said the Atlantean quietly, "so we will now return to your present time." As swiftly as we had left, we returned, with a curious Aileen awaiting news of the future.

"Well," Wen Shu asked, "what have you learned from that journey — indeed, what have you absorbed from all of the revelations, both past and future?"

I pondered before answering: "The past seems to indicate the points wherein I developed certain qualities and the future has shown how I might best utilize those qualities."

"Is that all you have gathered?" he questioned.

Looking at him swiftly to ascertain his mood, I replied hastily: "No — no, not at all. It does appear that my major task is to indicate to Man the need to bring his thought patterns under control, if he wishes to avoid the awful conflict which lies ahead."

He smiled at me benevolently. "Indeed that is so. Since the latter days of the Atlantean era, Man has battled with his thought patterns. So far, he has failed to master them." He paused a moment then said: "One further point that we must make is the foolishness demonstrated by Man on a growing scale, in discarding his varying crafts, blindly following Mammon into the era of mass production."

I stared at this, and asked: "What exactly do you mean? Is it so very wrong to mass produce? It certainly provides many with comforts they could not otherwise enjoy."

He sighed. "These are the illusions fed to Man by the Ahriamanic forces. In such a manner they turn Man aside from realities. The craftsman, not finding any market for his carefully hand-produced goods, abandons his trade and turns into an automaton in an effort to keep his head above the waters of gross materialism. Within the new Age, all craftsmen will be greatly prized, they will range with the highest in the land. The wise among them will train the young to follow after them, in order that their crafts might continue. Carry this message to your craftsmen, my son. Deter them from the path of illusion if you can."

"Hmmm, that's a tall order. How does one achieve that?" I asked doubtfully.

"By becoming a craftsman yourself. Apply yourself to your study, develop your healing craft, combine it with the art of teaching, and then instruct those who will in turn come towards you. Give your brother Man the gift of wholeness and you in turn will be whole," he said. He waited a moment while I digested this, then resumed speaking.

"One further point, knowing your great need for proof of our statements," he said, giving me a gentle smile. "In the future there will be placed upon your path many who study the ancient art of astrology. Not the foolishness which seeks to foretell the future in a mundane manner, but those who study the esoteric aspect of this ancient science. Listen to what they have to tell, my son, for many will bring you great evidence of the changes which lie ahead. Above all, be courageous in your labours. The warrior you have been many times in your past; draw on that hidden strength and fight against the encroaching tide of darkness.

"Our revelations are at an end. The task is now yours to fulfil. We shall always be at your side in your hour of need, but we shall not return in this manner again. Good luck on your journeys, my son — achieve . . . achieve . . . ." They all faded from view and Aileen stared at me in some astonishment, not knowing the full tale and surprised that this was the end of the communications.

Chapter 32

I carefully perused the manuscript, which in a sense had leapt into print out of the recesses of my mind. So many memories reawakened by this conscious review refused to die and I longed for the Brothers to make their reappearance. True to their word, I had not seen them for many a year, although on the astral plane during the sleep-state I often conversed with Wen Shu. My beloved teacher had also passed over and I was left alone to contemplate the happenings of the past.

Occasionally, an astrologer did cross my path, but apart from providing a chart which confirmed much that had been foretold by the Brothers, little of note appeared. Wearily I placed the manuscript in a drawer, which I carefully locked. "I would not wish it to fall into the wrong hands," I muttered to myself, and set about returning to a normal way of life. What I was to do with the finished product of many months of labour I did not know. 'Perhaps the Brothers will tell me' I thought caustically — knowing full well that they would not.

For some months I endeavoured to live my former life, but all that had hitherto satisfied now seemed empty and without purpose. I continually sought satisfaction in illusionary pleasures, only to wind up even more discontented. Realizing that some force was turning me away from such pursuits and as it seemed to be the vogue, I began to attend talks and discussions on spiritual approaches for the coming Age. During one week-end seminar I found myself in conversation with a tall, studious young man, whose gaunt frame and piercing eyes gave him the appearance of a modern-day Merlin.

Here was someone who lived for his astrological pursuits and his conversation was dotted with the most outrageous statements relating to global change, following great planetary conjunctions which he indicated lay ahead in the near future. Feeling that here was one of those predicted to make their appearance upon my path, I asked him penetrating questions relating to the many predictions he cast into his conversation, like seeds upon the wind.

The majority of that week-end was spent in his company and for many weeks following I sought him out, for much that he had to say had a familiar ring to it.

"When do you feel that the greater changes will begin?" I asked him curiously.

"Oh," he answered airily, waving his hands in the air, "with the conjunction of Jupiter with Saturn in Libra."

"Ummm . . ." I replied, "and when do you feel that it is likely to take place?"

Giving me a piercing look he said: "January 1st, 1981, but the planets will be close again at two further points during that year."

"And what do you feel that this conjunction will bring about?" I questioned.

"Well," he answered slowly, "it is a most important significative event for what lies ahead of Man. In national life it will bring about revolutions, leading to changes in order and administration of world affairs." Stopping to observe the effect of his words upon me, he then continued. "Many of the changes will be beneficial in the long term."

Pondering his words I asked: "How?"

Sitting down with his charts about him he answered: "The beneficial effects stem from Jupiter, which encourages Man to change, to alter his manner of thinking, whereas Saturn brings reality. The formative principal of Saturn gives a prelude of benefits which follow. One important point to bear in mind is the fact that this conjunction, which will be nine degrees in Libra, has not occurred since 1158, which saw the conflict between Moslems and Christians, the beginning of the Great Crusades."

His words hit me like a shattering blow. "Moslems . . . and Christians . . .?" Back into my mind swept all the prognostications relating to the rebirth of Islam. I swallowed hard. "Will that be an instantaneous thing?"

He smiled at me. "Of course not — it will build up; the effects are likely to be long term, though."

Deciding that I had to know more I asked: "What are the benefits that you spoke of?"

Delighted at my interest he continued: "Mankind will commence to become mentally active — his methods of communication may even tend to be unconventional."

"What do you mean by that?" I asked swiftly.

Gazing at me curiously, he answered: "Well, some may commence to receive telepathic messages — from those other than humans." Pausing a moment to see if his words were registering, he continued: "This will not happen immediately, but gradually, as part of the transition from our current 'earthy' outlook, towards one more conversant with the mental age which lies ahead."

I considered his words. "Perhaps I may not be considered so mad after all!" I muttered to myself.

Not understanding why I said this he stared at me for a while before he proceeded. "There is a much more important conjunction ahead in late 1982."

"What would that be?" I enquired, looking at him with interest.

"That will be between Saturn and Pluto, again in Libra, which will occur on the eighth of November and it is a conjunction which will indicate the great changes to come in the world. This is largely due to the limiting and controlling effect of Saturn being forced to combine with the explosive, clearing effect of Pluto."

I could not comprehend this. "I am not an astrologer — can you be a little more precise?"

Sighing exasperatedly he replied: "Pluto is the planet of transformation and regeneration — he eliminates. However, this planet's ability to achieve such action upon Earth has been held back for some considerable time, at least to a certain degree, by the limiting effect of Saturn. This limitation upon Pluto will continue until the major conjunctions of Saturn with Uranus in 1988 and in the following year, of Saturn with Neptune. Following these, the full powers of Pluto will be unleashed."

"What will be the result of those?" I asked.

"Major earthquakes — world wide," was his terse reply.

Shocked, I gazed at him almost disbelievingly. Was this man reading my mind? I wondered, for so much that he threw lightly into the air related to situations long indicated by the Brothers. Swallowing hard I pressed him: "Then there is nothing to fear until that time?"

"Oh heavens, yes, of course there is," he responded cheerily, almost as though he was discussing events upon a far distant planet. "Before that we have some violent changes coming up in February 1982, when Jupiter conjuncts Uranus and the changes wrought by this will be far more sudden and violent than those set in motion by the conjunction of Jupiter with Saturn in 1981."

"Why should that be?" I asked quietly.

"Because it will be the conjunction of Judgement and Originality. It will also produce the growth of unorthodox ideas, particularly in the field of religion and much of Mankind will begin to respond to 'New Age' thinking which will then spread rapidly through the world. Many will become interested in philosophical forms of study and it will possibly see the growth of creative and inventive powers in Man. What is more important, Man as an individual will come to the fore and many will break free of accepted ideas and ideals."

"That sounds interesting, but why should we fear that?" I asked, greatly curious.

"Largely because those who hold the seats of power — religious or otherwise — will fight Man's right to be an individual, to 'do his own thing'. Their power lies in dominance, they will fight to retain it. A lot of conflict will result."

I pondered upon his words, for it did seem to blend with much the Atlantean had endeavoured to teach me. Perhaps this was the beginning of positive thought control in Man.

He interrupted my train of thought. "This will all be compounded in January 1984 when Jupiter is conjunct Neptune, for this conjunction will speed up the many reformations taking place within the world. It will increase Man's awareness of injustice — and this is often the precursor to wars. On the other hand many will alter their manner of thinking, becoming more concerned with others, and less concerned with self. It will also bring about a dissolution of accepted concepts in the minds of Mankind and with it all comes an expansion of spiritual awareness: Man will have the opportunity to become aware of the real self and his true purpose upon Earth."

I stared hard at him. His words were almost those uttered many times by the Brothers. Could they perhaps be influencing him at this time? Shaking my head in puzzlement I answered, "Well, it all sounds a very heartening time for Man, doesn't it?"

"Not really," was his rather disconcerting reply, "for this conjunction will also bring a great deal of deception to the world. You will have the situation where one great nation will deceive another as to its true intent, but much worse — that nation will also deceive its own people — so determined are its rulers to maintain total power."

I looked rather despondent at this comment, but this did not deter him from continuing his tale. "These situations will be compounded by the move of Pluto into Scorpio, which is his natural home. It will be a tempestuous time for the planet; we shall experience political hell on Earth and the food situation will become very difficult, with famine in many places. All this will be accompanied by geophysical changes coupled with great upheavals in the weather patterns."

I shook my head in shock and disbelief. Could I never escape these gloomy predictions? Here, in a differing manner, were all the grim tales I had been fed for years by my spirit mentors.

I sat quietly for some considerable time, contemplating his words, whilst he busied himself among the charts.

"If you think those conjunctions are bad, wait till you hear this!" he exclaimed.

"Oh no!" I muttered, "not more. What else have you found to add to the despair of Mankind?" I asked, in a joking manner which had an undercurrent of fear within it.

"Those conjunctions I spoke of earlier, between Saturn and Uranus in 1988 and Saturn with Neptune in 1989, both of which will take place in Capricorn," he replied.

I sat up wearily, realizing that there was no manner of escape from this flood of information.

"What will they bring with them?" I asked.

Gazing at his charts he said concisely: "They have ominous overtones for world commerce, particularly those countries ruled by Capricorn."

This latter comment was something new to me. "What exactly do you mean by 'those countries ruled by Capricorn'? Do planets affect countries too?"

"But of course they do!" He looked at me in disbelief, almost as though this information was common knowledge.

"Oh," I replied diffidently. "Which countries will this conjunction affect, then?"

Glancing at his notes he answered: "Austria, Greece, India, Japan and Spain."

"But why do you suggest that these conjunctions will have a greater effect upon Man than the others you have mentioned?" I asked, mystified.

Pursing his lips tightly, he replied: "Because they are so very close together they will be felt almost simultaneously, and their effects will last for a very long time. These conjunctions free Pluto to gather opportunity to bring about regeneration through elimination, for in 1989 he will be in his natural home, Scorpio. His opportunities will be provided by these very conjunctions. You see, Saturn brings with him disaster and responsibility for Man. Uranus brings vast change, and with it, illumination, whilst Neptune brings confusion, yet provides inspiration for future action."

"If I may say so, it is a little vague. What action will they actually have upon the planet?" I queried, somewhat hesitantly.

Sighing at my total inability to grasp his point, he answered wearily: "It will be the time when very great upheavals will occur. We will experience major earthquakes and subsequent tidal waves, much worse than those experienced earlier. There will be a gradual build-up of freak weather conditions, it will no longer be possible to predict weather patterns as we do now. We may even see some lands vanish overnight."

"Good heavens!" was my only comment, as I stared at him. Then I asked: "Why do you say this?"

Grimly he continued: "Because these conjunctions herald chaos in the world. They will also bring about vast political changes, which in turn will lead to great upsets in governmental affairs world wide."

I gazed at him humorously. "Do you manage to sleep at night — with all this information ticking away in your mind?"

He countered my comment with a wide grin and continued: "At three points during 1993, Uranus is conjunct Neptune and this will bring about disruption of governments and changes in the constitutional rule of countries. Eventually this will lead to a period within which will rise the opportunity for the foundation of new methods of government, coupled with new and more positive outlooks, based upon new Age awareness. Unfortunately, it will also bring about earthquakes, natural disasters and wars, in addition to the break-up of world conditions as we know them."

"In other words — total chaos!" I commented bluntly.

He nodded. "There will, however, come much spiritual aspiration during this period. When all is dark, Man turns to God. There will be a new urge within Man to seek spiritual understanding and with this will come the need to eradicate old religious thought patterns."

"Well, that will certainly be a positive step forward," I commented. "Will we achieve it?"

He answered quietly: "It will not be an easy task, for although Man will be searching for a new concept for life, those who direct his spiritual life will oppose all thought of change. Truth will eventually emerge and the established doctrines will finally be rejected."

"I would like to think that what you suggest will really come about," I said. "With religious patterns as they are at present, I cannot see it happening."

Swiftly he replied: "It will be aided in late 1994, when Jupiter is conjunct Plato. That will be a prophetic conjunction and Man will become deeply involved with the study of the 'collective unconsciousness' and as the result, begin to get a true perspective of values. But most of all, this conjunction seeks to prepare the world for the solar eclipse which will take place in 1999."

"What effect will that have?" I asked — again mystified. "I was not aware that a solar eclipse was such an important sign."

Once more shaking his head in disbelief, he answered: "A solar eclipse in a fixed sign is said to have long-lasting effects and this one will take place in the fire sign of Leo."

"So?" I countered.

"An eclipse in the fire sign of Leo indicates the end of a ruler or an organization," he said.

Again not understanding, I stared at him. "I told you that I am not an astrologer, so I have no idea what you are implying," I said, my turn to be impatient.

"Oh very well!" he answered somewhat pettishly. "Leo is the

ruler of Italy — and Rome. The eclipse will be opposition Uranus and square Mars and Saturn. It indicates the end of the powerful rule of the Catholic Church."

My face blanched at this. The Atlantean had indicated this situation and here was the manner in which it would be brought about.

Pressing on without concern he continued: "I have also charted this period and there is the indication of the formation of a Planetary Grand Cross at this time." The latter he said in hushed tones, almost as though he had located news of the end of the world. Before I could ask, he said: "Such a formation is always the portent of great change for the race of Man." He sat back quietly, watching the effect of his words upon me.

"When do you say that this will occur?" I asked, ignoring his dramatic manner.

"I locate it as taking place on the 11th August 1999 — just a couple months behind that predicted by Nostradamus . . . ."

I jolted upright at this comment. "What did Nostradamus forecast for that time?"

"Oh," he cried, "that is quite a famous prediction; let me see if I can remember it all. 'In the year 1999 and seven months, from the sky will come the great king of terror. He will bring back to life the great king of the Mongols. Before and afterwards, war reigns happily'."

I stared at him in utter disbelief. This man must be reading the recesses of my mind. Why else did he relate so much which the Brothers had brought forward? Yet had they not advised me to watch for astrologers who would confirm? What was I to make of all this? My mind was turning over at such an amazing rate that I could no longer absorb any further information, so I took my leave of him very swiftly, thanking him automatically for the evening as I did so.

Following that time, I spent every available moment checking the validity of the statements made by my friend with those astrologers whom I could contact, although I realized that all I did was to postpone the inevitable day when I would have to take my tale to the public. All I uncovered added further proof to that which had commenced in the mists of my youth, past and future mingling to produce a pattern which could not be avoided. Obviously, it was vital that I must set the pattern, seek opportunities to serve my brother Man, and share with love, the knowledge fed to me by those loving Brothers of Light who had guided my steps through time.

In Conclusion

Whether that which you have read is fact or fantasy, I must leave the reader to decide. I have endeavoured to show that one's thoughts and actions, be they good or bad, return for payment, thus giving the necessity for control of thought and subsequent action to avoid unnecessary suffering in future lifetimes, at the same time benefiting Mankind as a whole, for we are all inextricably linked, one with another — therefore the thought or action of one must of necessity affect all.

This is the story of my evolvement, but it could well have been yours. Each has to find his or her own level and commitments in this incarnation, for as the Nazarene said: "Seek and ye shall find"; "Knock and it shall be opened unto you"; "Ask and ye shall receive." This is your task, as mine is being fulfilled in part by presenting to you the information which the Brothers have brought forward to me as a channel, for the benefit of Mankind.

If on completing this tale you have decided to try to control your own thought patterns in some measure, then my efforts have been worth while. If in addition to this you have begun to beam out light around the planet as part of your daily routine, then I am deeply grateful, and Mankind will be profoundly indebted to you.

Many will doubt that much which is set down within these pages could have taken place, or will come to pass. Before passing judgement, study carefully your daily press; note the growing inhumanity to Man, wherein value for life has been superseded by greed for power. The law of the jungle is once more beginning to dominate our lives. We cannot wait for others to change; so *we* must change — in our thoughts and in our daily actions. If you will spend a little time each day in analysing your thought patterns, you will see how often — albeit unintentionally — they are destructive. A lesson in itself.

Above all, I would ask that you maintain a daily vigil of light for the planet. Draw your friends and loved ones into this — encourage them to share light with the planet and all life upon it — please.

Let us HEAL THE EARTH — for our continued existence depends upon it.